LOST WALTZ

Archduke Franz Josef of Austria in New York.

LOST WALTZ

A Story of Exile

by

BERTITA HARDING

"Truly, defeat alone can extend our limits . . ."
—Dr. Serge Voronoff

THE BOBBS-MERRILL COMPANY
Publishers

INDIANAPOLIS   NEW YORK

THE CORNWALL PRESS, INC., CORNWALL, N. Y.

To

Their Imperial and Royal Highnesses
ARCHDUKE AND ARCHDUCHESS FRANZ JOSEF

WHOSE HELP WITH THE MATERIAL FOR THIS BOOK
AMOUNTED TO ACTUAL COLLABORATION.

List of Illustrations

7

LOST WALTZ

Chapter One

Pat

SOLEDAD DID NOT KNOW that she was beautiful. Nor, for that matter, did anyone else. It would have been difficult indeed, even for eyes trained in such matters, to pierce the forbidding exterior which the convent school of Santa Brígida imposed upon its wards. The children who attended Santa Brígida were orphans, supported by charity. Their training was attuned to that simple fact. Since no easy path was likely to await them on stepping out into the world, it would have been folly to teach them the ways of vanity.

"The ways of vanity are folly in any case," said Mother Porfiria, prioress of the convent. It was Mother Porfiria who designed the hideous gray garments that shrouded the girls' young bodies, hiding every vestige of contour and grace. She also imposed a standard coiffure upon her charges, demanding that their hair be yanked back into a braid and—in the case of girls above fourteen—pinned up in a tight bun. The skinned-rat look thus imparted was admirably suited to the timorous dejection of all Santa Brígida orphans. Since they had nothing to expect, they might as well not look as if they expected anything.

This was certainly true of Soledad. At seventeen she would have been startled to know that her face and brow were shaped to delight a sculptor. Had she possessed a mirror (none existed in the convent) it would have told her that the slant of her hazel eyes was neither doelike nor meek, but touched with a certain daring allure. As for her figure, hidden in the sack that—through courtesy of Mother Porfiria—passed for a dress, it had points not generally stressed in ecclesiastic art. Here was no model for a

II

gaunt Gothic madonna, but a veiled masterpiece of pagan delight.

To be sure, at Santa Brígida no one, least of all Soledad, indulged in such carnal contemplations. There was something about the orphanage that discouraged flights of fancy and even paled what bloom attached itself to fact. Often you were hardly aware of your own name, particularly if you had been brought in as a foundling with no identification on your clothes.

This had not been the case with Soledad. She was the daughter of Basque peasants who had been killed with two of their other children in an avalanche that buried their village of Ancuello in the Pyrenees. Ten-year-old Soledad had been dug from the debris—miraculously alive—and shipped with other victims to the nearest first-aid station and thence to the convent. Here the parish priest of her native village attested to the girl's name, age and antecedents; she was an orphan, yes, but not an outcast waif left on somebody's doorstep. . . .

At Ancuello everyone had called her Chole, which was the diminutive for Soledad. But in the convent register she had been entered by her full name of María de la Soledad Gola y Mendáriz, after both her parents and the blessed Virgin of Solitude. To the other children at the orphanage she was Chole too. The nuns, however, and particularly Mother Porfiria, insisted upon formality. They disapproved of nicknames.

It was Mother Porfiria who addressed herself to Chole on a fateful day in November 1918.

"Soledad," she said in measured tones, "next week you will be seventeen."

"Yes, Reverend Mother," answered the girl, making an awkward curtsy.

"It is time that we found a place for you in the world," the prioress went on.

Chole felt a flush suffuse her cheeks. "But I have yet to study another year—before I get my certificate of graduation which will permit me to enter the Escuela Normal at Santander." She was ambitious; she wanted to become a teacher, trained at the best normal school in the Basque Provinces. But before aspiring to enrollment at Santander she must complete the required preparatory courses. To leave even an orphan school without a diploma meant little choice in professions beyond that of servant girl. Chole had other plans.

Mother Porfiria tugged at her coif and repeatedly cleared her throat. The thing she had to say was obviously not easy. On November eleventh another of Europe's chronic wars—this time a dire catastrophe of world dimensions—had come to an end. Armistice terms and their acceptance were being proclaimed by press and wireless. This meant that refugees from the defeated belligerent countries would pour into neutral zones to escape reprisals. Already a caravan of war orphans was on its way from hospitable but overcrowded Switzerland, where not another soul could find asylum. Only yesterday the Red Cross Headquarters at Geneva had sent frantic calls for help to the Scandinavian capitals and Madrid. Before morning every convent in Spain had received an appeal to throw open its doors to the flood of innocents made homeless by adult savagery. Upwards of three hundred children were to be billeted at Santa Brígida alone. This meant not only a doubling up in dormitories but a rigorous weeding out of charges considered old enough to fend for themselves.

"In times like these," the prioress summed up the predicament, "we must dispense with graduations."

Chole was dismissed.

She returned to the cubicle she shared with two companions, their narrow cots separated by homespun curtains. In adjoining dormitories other girls packed their flimsy belongings and prepared to leave. There was furtive whispering. Mariana La Prieta (Black Mary Ann)—a highly imaginative Catalan—had heard a rumor.

"They say," she reported, with dark eyes popping, "that we're to be sent to Madrid as special wards of the Queen!"

There was a breathless gasp from the younger girls. "You mean the Hospicio San Jacinto, of which Her Majesty is patroness?"

"Rubbish," interjected a skeptic. "The best seamstresses and lacemakers come out of San Jacinto. What is the Queen to do with a bunch of untrained provincials like us?"

The speaker was a blowzy wench with a broad face and flaming red hair that bore vivid testimony to the Visigoth invasions of more than a thousand years ago, when blond Vandals, Suevi, Alans and Franks infiltrated throughout northern Spain, imparting a fresh pigment to ancient Celtic and Iberian blood.

"Carola is right," concurred another. "What would they want with us in Madrid?"

Mariana was optimistic. "The Queen's hospitals need nurses; perhaps we'll be recruited and sent into training——"

A loud laugh came from the redheaded girl. It was a raw laugh with an undertone. "Training? That's rich! You mean for wet nurses, don't you? Remember, Basque women give the best milk in Europe!"

Silence met this shocking remark. Carola was always saying things like that: bold, startling things that betokened an uncommon knowledge of a world with which at her age (she was scarcely fifteen) she ought to have been less familiar.

She was a strange one, this Carola, differing from the others in many ways, not the least of which was the fact that she had only one name. Carola. That was all. How she had come to Santa Brígida, or whence, nobody knew. Her biographical record in the convent register was as bare as the naked urchin that had been found years ago cowering under a length of burlap outside the porter's lodge. Though the child did not know her age, they had judged her, after one glimpse of the poor emaciated body, to be six or eight. Subsequent observation of her alarming precocity had caused a radical revision of this estimate. It had also confronted the good nuns of the Order of Saint Bridget with a source of constant dismay, for the foundling was to become a problem child.

It was with considerable relief that Mother Porfiria today had added Carola's name to the list of convent charges who must be dispatched in order to make room for the incoming refugees. As yet no one but Carola's roommate, Chole, had noticed this. Chole noticed everything. She had observed, for example, that all the pupils engaged just now in packing their possessions were between seventeen and nineteen years old. Carola alone did not belong in this age group. Yes, the distraught nuns were ridding themselves of a poser they could not cope with. Carola was too much for them.

As for Chole's own destination and that of the other girls as well, neither Carola nor Black Mary Ann had guessed right. The Queen of Spain did not elect to make them her especial charges, and at Madrid's hospitals the supply of applicants for nursing duty far exceeded any demand, hence no new candidates were welcomed from the provinces. Mother Porfiria had known this all along, of course, since she had personally filled out a questionnaire sent by a leading employment agency for domestics in Barcelona.

It was a first-rate bureau, Mother Porfiria told herself. Her girls would be in good hands. They would be placed as cooks, chambermaids, laundresses and nannies in some of Catalonia's best homes.

True, servant work ranked at the bottom of the social scale, despised by many.

But, after all, what could orphans expect?

Chapter Two

THE ARMISTICE DID NOT, as might have been anticipated, ring out with peals of joy through the world.

Only in the more remote corners of the earth, where neither hunger nor horror had stalked for four long years, and where war had seemed only a distant nightmare dreamed by someone else, did the news rebound upon happy ears. Noise, paper streamers and revelry filled streets as though at carnival time, while strangers hugged and danced with one another in borrowed ecstasy. This was true primarily in the Americas where, except for Canada and the United States, participation in the conflict had been diplomatic rather than military. Thus Rio de Janeiro, Buenos Aires, Santiago and Mexico City celebrated with unaffected spirits the lifting of a burden they had scarcely felt.

But in Europe it was otherwise. Even the victor nations had bled too heavily to find triumph undimmed by mourning. If the boulevards of Paris and the squares of London echoed with laughter, as did the great avenues extending from New York to San Francisco, hysteria joined the din and disguised tears behind the mask of merriment. Soldiers, mutilated in battle, broke into song—but in a minor key. Though the pain had stopped, they were still without their limbs.

It was worse, of course, with the vanquished. To them cessation of hostilities brought a numbness and apathy scarcely approaching even relief. When all that has been spent proves itself misspent, nothing remains save utter negation. A futile war that is lost, a peace not won, wear the same face. It is the face of frustration, retouched by the gall and wormwood of defeat.

The once proud Austro-Hungarian Empire wore this miserable face, for it had been within its borders that the great war had started. Not that the ancient Danube monarchy had yearned to turn from waltzes to world contest; soldiering was at best a dreary business, and nothing could have been farther from the mind of tired octogenarian Emperor Franz Joseph than to embark upon exploits of Napoleonic dimensions. Sarajevo? The punitive campaign against Serbia? It had been the result of a private feud, almost a family vendetta, over the murder of an archduke on a Bosnian street.

Franz Joseph had not counseled going to war. Indeed, he had counseled the Archduke not to go to Bosnia. But once the tragedy had occurred, parliamentary pressure and national pride combined to force the Emperor's hand. Gavrilo Princip, the assassin, had been a Serb and a member of an insurgent Pan-Slav society operating within Austria's own boundaries. It was time to clean house.

Housecleaning may be fraught with danger, as at times it disturbs smoldering ashes hidden in ancient chimney pots or flues, from which feeble sparks can be dislodged and fanned into agents of flaming destruction—provided there are eager and co-operating winds. The Europe of 1914 had been full of such winds, ready to blast the most innocent ember into a blazing torch. The pyrotechnics that followed were to make a historic holocaust.

Franz Joseph died before the fires were put out. The tumbling house fell upon younger shoulders which were irked by so unwelcome a burden: the Emperor Karl inherited the war, but he wished no part of it. Since he had had no hand in the outbreak of hostilities, his impulses were not frozen by stubbornness or pride. He humbly sued for peace. But the high winds by now had turned into a hurricane.

The conflagration sped on, eating its way over half the earth, until men could no longer see themselves or their objectives through the thickening smoke. In the end there would be left only a choking weariness and a blind sense of rebellion against whatever force had dared let loose the demons of war. For Europe's impoverished multitudes these demons were embodied in the rich. As betrayed patriotism waned into disillusion, class hatred grew and became vocal. Its dissonance marred the clear clarion call of peace.

Yes, Armistice celebrants put up a brave show throughout Continental capitals, but behind them rode the tumbrils of revolution.

No one knew this better than the children of the Archduke and Archduchess Leopold Salvator, at Castle Wilhelminenberg on the Galitzin Hill near Vienna. Their father, a Habsburg of the collateral Tuscan line and a nephew of the patriarchal Emperor Franz Joseph, had for many years been Inspector General of the Austrian Artillery. He was also Commander of the 18th Infantry Regiment, Knight of the Golden Fleece, and Chevalier of the Black Eagle. But these distinctions were as nothing compared to the fact that Leopold Salvator was husband to the Infanta Blanca of Castile, Princess de Bourbon and daughter of Don Carlos, the Pretender to the throne of Spain.

The Infanta, now Archduchess, Blanca was a woman of parts. Handsome in an imperious way, she had sharply piercing eyes, an aquiline profile, and an extraordinary mind bordering on the brilliant. She had also something rare in both royal and unroyal circles: common sense.

But, first and foremost, the Infanta was (ten times) a mother. This achievement in itself had not been easily arrived at, inasmuch as Leopold Salvator was an inveterate traveler. His army job, particularly during his younger days, kept him in constant rotation from one of the Empire's provinces to another, serving an average of three years in each. In order to keep the growing family not only together, but at its dynastic production peak, the household remained obligingly on the move. For royalty, unashamedly aware of the first principle of survival, namely a proper birth rate, never fails to survive. Whether in full power or disgrace or banishment, its children are its future—while indifference to nature's most fundamental demand, parenthood, has brought extinction (often within a few generations) to hardier proletarian strains.

Certainly the Infanta's obstetric record deserves tabulation. It was said that the Emperor's exchequer had instructions to bestow a million kronen upon an archduchess on the occasion of each happily terminated pregnancy, which may well have reflected upon the ratio of Habsburg fertility. In any case, the Leopold Salvator offspring, all of them healthy and destined to reach adulthood, were, according to age and birthplace:

> Dolores—May 5, 1891, at Lemberg
> Immaculata—September 9, 1892, at Lemberg
> Margareta—May 8, 1894, at Lemberg
> Rainer—November 21, 1895, at Agram
> Leopold—January 30, 1897, at Agram
> Maria Antonia—July 13, 1899, at Agram
> Anton—March 20, 1901, at Vienna
> Assunta—August 10, 1902, at Vienna
> Franz Josef—February 4, 1905, at Vienna
> Carlos—December 4, 1909, at Vienna

Between the last two, Franz Josef and Carlos, there existed a state of mild rivalry for the place of the pampered baby chick. For a few years Franz Josef had been the Benjamin, basking in the collective attention of parents, brothers, sisters, cousins, uncles and aunts, as well as enjoying the sole ministrations of old Resi, the veteran nursery fixture. As a nanny, Resi was something special. Long ago she had discarded her identity (she was Fräulein Therese Matte from Gmunden) and every vestige of a personal life. Her days were wrapped in selfless devotion to the archducal flock. One after one, ten small sleepy heads had been pillowed on her ample bosom (Resi was round as a butterball) and each in succession had outgrown her care, until, for almost five years, small Franz Josef seemed to be the last. Upon him Resi lavished a nostalgic excess of tenderness, dreading to see him grow. What would she do when there were no more infants in this house to tend? She, who had found no time to rear a family of her own . . .

The matter preyed upon her and she prayed to God. She also took the issue up with the specific patron of children, Saint Bartholomew. In addition, she was not above dropping sly hints about the premises, preferably within hearing of her tolerant employers. Two decades of service gave her the prerogative of occasionally forgetting her place and broadcasting a piece of her mind.

"To think," lamented Resi, "that we have five girls, but only four boys! *Ten* would be such a neat, round number. . . ."

This commentary would be accompanied by heavenward glances of great piety, as well as a succession of eloquent sighs.

The Archduchess Blanca, who was a realist, faced things squarely. "If we did have ten little ones," she mused, "Resi will give us to understand that there ought to be a round dozen——"

Nevertheless, whether by act of God or Habsburg submission to Resi's authority, the baby Carlos had come along to enliven the nursery and bring delight to all. All, that is, save five-year-old Franz Josef.

To Franz Josef the diapered and gurgling newcomer was an unmitigated bore. With Carlos around, his own baby days, prolonged until now by indulgent elders, were definitely over. Quite abruptly he no longer had even a nursemaid, since Resi's time was taken up with her new charge. Like his older brothers, Franz Josef was entrusted to the care of a manservant who would in later years be replaced by a personal valet.

The manservant was a Czech named Josef Beneš, who answered to the diminutive of Pepi.

Pepi had possibilities. For one thing, he understood Franz Josef's miff at having been chucked so unceremoniously from the nursery. In various and subtle ways Pepi strove to make up for this bitter childhood sorrow. For example, when he swept up the room each morning he invited "his" archduke to straddle the broomstick at the brush end and thus glide along for the ride.

"*Reibung!*" he shouted in warning, before executing a wide arc. "Curve coming!"

This wonderful feat earned him the child's quick confidence and love. Soon, in fact, Franz Josef's admiration for the resourceful Pepi, whose inventiveness in the matter of games was prodigious, had grown so great that he yearned to share the servant's nickname. In no time at all he became the Archduke Pepi.

It was during this period that the children were taken occasionally to Schönbrunn for a visit with the Archduke Pepi's godfather, Emperor Franz Joseph. This proved always a memorable event as the aged monarch had become,

even in the family circle, a legendary figure. There was
much about him to admire, for he was majestic and benign
like Father Christmas. Then there were his famous side-
burns and clean-shaven chin, which lent him a picturesque
and altogether unique appearance, so that anyone else wearing such a beard would be pointed out with the remark "He
looks just like the Emperor Franz Joseph!" But most of all
the children loved His Majesty's magnificently polished
black patent-leather shoes. They had the shiniest toes in the
world. You could practically see your own reflection mir-
rored in their high gloss.

Once a year a gala banquet took place at the Hofburg to
which all the monarch's grandchildren, nephews and nieces
above the age of fourteen were bidden (at this age you had
your first footman standing behind your chair, serving no one
but you). At more intimate meals, however, smaller children too were present and thrilled by the sight of their liege.

There was only one drawback to dining with the Emperor. His Majesty ate little and very rapidly, with etiquette
forbidding everyone else to touch a morsel after the imperial
fork had been laid down. The result was that you always
went away from Schönbrunn hungry, as most of the food
traveled back to the palace kitchens on your plate.

Another and equally disturbing factor was the aged sire's
tendency to drowse off in his chair, sometimes at the end of
the soup course. This meant the end of dinner as well.

"Der Kaiser ist eingeschlafen!" announced the imperial
chamberlain with a momentous air. ("His Majesty is
asleep!")

This information was rather gratuitous as the snoring at
the head of the table could leave no possible doubt. It was
the inevitable signal for a general exodus.

"The next time we come to Schönbrunn," said Papa, "let's bring sandwiches."

Nevertheless for the Archduke Pepi each visit to his god-father remained an unforgettable event, enhanced by the proud realization that he was the Emperor's only godchild and, by the same token, the only one to bear his famous name. The minor difference of *ph* being replaced by *f* was dictated by the rules of modernized Austrian spelling.

Speaking of spelling, Mama had begun to worry about the Archduke Pepi's education. Joy rides on the end of a manservant's broom were all very well, but like his brothers and sisters before him, the young Franz Josef must be taken more sternly in hand. Already he had been too spoiled by Resi and Beneš to learn his alphabet unless someone sang it to him.

At best, due to their difference in ages, the children presented a problem in pedagogy. All of them received elementary training at the hands of a tutor, who had been a household adjunct for almost as long as the perennial Resi, yet had been pensioned on account of ill health. A new teacher would have to be found for the Archduke Pepi.

Mama looked after the matter herself. Going straight to one of the public schools, she located a young man of twenty-five, named Karl Stepanek, who suited her specifications. After due negotiations Stepanek joined the household on Galitzin Hill. Normally, after assimilating their ABCs, numbers, and whatever else their tutor's acumen could impart, the girls had been turned over to a governess named Fräulein Kurtz, while the boys came under the care of Pater Gregor. The latter was a Benedictine monk on indefinite leave from the abbey of his order at Kremsmünster.

Parental discipline likewise figured prominently in the

children's upbringing. There were daily reading periods with Mama, whose Spanish accent injected an early note of cosmopolitanism into the Viennese setting. Whether she read aloud in French, German, or even a smattering of Hungarian, there was no mistaking the Infanta: she always sounded Spanish. This was partly because Mama could not pronounce the letter *h,* always silent in a Latin tongue. To compromise, she either skipped it altogether, Cockney fashion, or produced a guttural *ch* as in the Scottish *loch.* It remained for her sons and daughters to decide at a tender age which was the better part of virtue: whether to call Mama's mistakes and, at risk of being disrespectful, help her correct them, or tactfully and politely to duplicate her linguistic lapses.

The problem was of course automatically solved by Mama's unassailable majesty. The daughter of Don Carlos —in whose veins flowed the blood of Ferdinand and Isabella, not to mention a substantial dash of Bourbon—could not be corrected. If every breath she drew was irrevocably Hispanic, the shade of Cervantes himself could feel only gratification.

Of greater importance than her accent was the Infanta's choice of reading matter. For entertainment of the younger children she kept on hand the *Contes de Fées* or fairy tales published by Hachette's famed Bibliothèque Rose Illustrée. This fascinating gold-beveled edition was garnished with steel engravings that were either of a cloying sweetness, adored by the very young, or else capable of arousing the most horrendous fright.

Here were the old familiar stories, dear to childhood everywhere. But with a difference. Due to the Infanta's zeal for variation, which in her case was phonetically no variation at all, the listeners became at times confused. Mama liked reading the same tale successively in four tongues, which called for mental agility on the part of her audience. Quite early the children learned that Cinderella was at the same time Cendrillon in French, Cenicienta in Spanish and Aschenbroedel in German. Equally Little Red Riding Hood became Petit Chaperon Rouge, Caperucita Roja, or Rotkäppchen, while the dread figure of Bluebeard reappeared as Barbe Bleue, Barba Azul, or the ominous Blaubart.

To sort out and comprehend the hodgepodge of Mama's daily conversation became indeed second nature to the growing archdukes and their sisters. It simply became a habit with them to think in quadruplicate.

Evenings, after the toddlers had gone to bed, Mama selected stronger literary fare. She read to the older children from history books, particularly those dealing with the French Revolution. Marie Antoinette, erstwhile Archduchess of Austria, was conjured up before her awed descendants as a reminder of the fate that might befall all who walked in high places. The guillotine, the Terror, the long blood bath unleashed by the Paris Commune, returned specterlike to haunt all who recklessly boasted: "This is the twentieth century. Such things can't happen now."

But the Infanta's mood was not always so grim. She had a vast store of legends and anecdotes, each pointing up some gentle moral for the benefit of inexperienced youth. As an illustration of the meek virtue of patience, a favorite incident with her was culled from the life of the "Biedermeier Emperor" Franz.

That unmartial gentleman had been confronted, in 1812, with the task of opposing Napoleon's sweep across Europe. For this purpose he spent several sleepless nights drafting a pungent plea to the Czar and the King of Prussia, enlisting their aid in freedom's common cause.

After prolonged and painstaking composition the document was at last finished, calling only for the Emperor's own signature. In the dim grayness of dawn His Majesty executed a fine flourish and spelled out the word *Franz*. Now for a sprinkling of sand to dry the script.

The monarch's hand reached across the writing table, only to collide with the arm of an oversolicitous secretary. In the confusion a dreadful thing happened. The secretary, flustered by his own awkwardness, seized the inkwell instead of the small sand crock. A moment later the damage was done, as a black lagoon covered the outspread papers.

Silence fell upon the room and within that silence the hapless servant shivered. Ministers and lofty dignitaries glared as they awaited an outburst of imperial wrath. But in another second the atmosphere had cleared.

"Das macht nix," murmured His Viennese Majesty, crinkling weary eyelids. *"Mir fangen halt wieder von vorn an*——" ("It doesn't matter. We'll just start over again——")

Chapter Three

THE LESSONS TAUGHT during those reading periods in Mama's little sitting room proved useful sooner than expected. The skies above Austria were growing dark: the debacle approached. No longer did the children have to be told what constitutes a "mob," for the Vienna streets teemed with roaming malcontents who railed against the war and the regime supposedly responsible for it. Everywhere was the harrowing, bleak face of hunger.

It made life in a castle quite incongruous.

At Schloss Wilhelminenberg there were eighty-six servants, all told. This included chauffeurs, grooms, stableboys, valets, cooks, maids, gardeners, gatekeepers, laundresses, dressmakers, mending women, and the nursemaid Resi. Most of these workers, with the exception of the valets, personal maids, and Resi, were housed in separate quarters adjoining the mews, some fifty meters below the archducal home. Daily an administrator set the wheels of the great estate in motion, taking stock of the produce from vegetable and fruit gardens, as well as budgeting the household's needs.

With increasing wartime shortages this was no small task. As early as 1916 Austria-Hungary had already forgotten what sugar, butter, eggs and white bread looked like, since most of these products were being drained off by the armies of a potent and demanding ally, Germany. The Magyar plains, known as the breadbasket of the Empire, furnished the bulk of foodstuffs for the Central Powers, causing a famine at home.

In Vienna the pinch was felt by rich and poor alike, since

28

bare grocery shelves could play no favorites. The aristocrat's porcelain plate, the peasant's wooden bowl, boasted the same pale turnip in identically rotating disguise—now diced, now boiled whole, mashed, or coaxed into a round patty. The coffee, brewed from toasted barley, chicory, potato skins and other less identifiable increments, tasted no more abominable in the porter's lodge than at the Emperor's table.

Yet even with such general scarcity, noblesse must still oblige, lest rumors spread concerning gastronomic orgies in high places. At Castle Wilhelminenberg, when the day's skimpy fare had been cooked and readied for serving, the help sat down to eat before anyone else. No echo here of Marie Antoinette's flippant, though perhaps apocryphal, recommendation that the breadless reach for cake. They knew too much over at the manor house, either by sharpened instinct or through the Infanta's unending preoccupation with France, anno 1789, to risk anarchy on their own premises.

Such superficial precautions could not of course blot out the inequalities of centuries of feudal living. The pattern of Europe's society, even under the most benevolent conditions, was still that of master and slave. It was a bondage without chains, partly political in character, partly economic, largely habitual and endeared through tradition. In peacetime it worked—or seemed to work—till the next cataclysm of war. But when fear, misery and want descended upon mankind, that social order proved untenable. Too late the hasty, magnanimous gesture: the sharing of clothes, victuals and coal. Roused from complacency by sheer wretchedness, the proletariat was not easily assuaged. The outward motions of democracy on the part of the rich classes fooled no one. If nobody had fuel, winter was still more bearable in palaces than hovels. It left the tenants of the hovels not well disposed toward palaces. . . .

At Wilhelminenberg the trend of popular emotion percolated almost imperceptibly through everyone's consciousness. A subtle arrogance was first seen among stableboys and grooms, some of them veterans from the Russian or Italian front. They talked in disillusioned voices of treachery and sure defeat, but their rancor was not the first hot flame of hatred directed against some outward threat to the Fatherland; it was a cold fury, turned inward upon leaders who allowed murderous wars—again and yet again—to happen.

Conversations of this sort did not lift melancholy spirits. Listeners grumbled and gave vent to their own lightly cloaked cynicism, particularly regarding the appalling casualty lists pouring in from every battle sector. The poor and underprivileged (who made up the bulk of armies everywhere) were dying, as always, while their "betters" lived on to plot the conflicts of the future.

In wartime walls have ears. Though he was seldom at home, the Archduke Leopold Salvator knew well what went on in his garages, stables and mews. From his wife's letters, reaching him irregularly at the front, he became aware quite early of disintegration at home. It was of little help that his two eldest sons, Rainer and Leopold, served in the first line of battle, as artillery privates—without privilege or rank, which his own high office might have wangled for them; the Vienna populace had turned from a genial operetta audience that idolized its Graustark princelings into a sullen horde.

"It's just like that horrid mess in France," wrote the Infanta Blanca, missing no chance to point up her historic acumen. She knew exactly how poor Louis XVI must have felt.

To meet the threatening crisis she had already taken some precautionary steps. In every treatise on revolution, when the existing order toppled, there was mention of "incriminating papers" which brought calamity upon their owners. Could there be ominous writings at Wilhelminenberg? Not likely, since Archduke Leopold Salvator was not emperor, but merely a soldier taking orders from the state. Even so, one could never tell. With eagle eye the Infanta rummaged through trunks, cupboards and desk drawers, gathering every scrap, including her own girlhood letters from Spain. At night, after the servants had gone to bed, she descended into the palace basement and made a paper fire in the empty furnace. Only when a mound of dead ashes remained did she return upstairs.

She slept badly nowadays. For one thing, the family was not complete. With a husband and two sons at the front, the household seemed strangely unbalanced. Five daughters, Archduke Anton, and the baby Carlos were left—an excessively feminine world. If at least she had kept her second youngest, Franz Josef, to bolster the masculine element! But the Archduke Pepi was away at school, the only one of her children not educated at home.

It was awkward about Franz Josef. A gentle, sweet-tempered child, he in no way deserved being discriminated against. Yet circumstances combined to make his lot a difficult one. Having outgrown old Resi's ministrations, he next had been placed in the care of the tutor, Stepanek. But Carlos was growing too, and ready for Stepanek's pedagogy. In normal times this would have advanced Franz Josef, like his older brothers before him, into the classroom of Pater Gregor. Only there was no Pater Gregor any more. Early in the war the man-power shortage had become acute throughout Austria, calling for drastic measures. Lay brothers, friars and parish priests who could not perform military duties were summoned by their district heads to work in the fields. Pater Gregor had returned to Kremsmünster Abbey at harvest time. Instead of teaching algebra he dug potatoes.

This left Franz Josef without schooling.

Happily, before departing, Pater Gregor had offered a solution. The Jesuit Academy of Stella Matutina at Feldkirch, one of the few boarding schools that had survived wartime stringencies, still took in boys. As Feldkirch lay on the way to Kremsmünster he would be glad to enroll Franz Josef in person.

The Infanta looked doubtful. "A boarding school? I am not sure my husband would approve. And in any case, how much longer can the Jesuit Fathers run their establishment? Where do they get fuel and food?"

"Feldkirch is well forested, Your Highness," explained Pater Gregor. "The Jesuits cut their own wood and grow their kitchen needs."

Mama still wavered, though not for long. The next step in Franz Josef's tutelage would normally have been entrusted to an army officer, Captain Kurtz, whose sister served as governess to the young archduchesses. But Kurtz, currently Anton's tutor, would soon return to active duty at the front, joining his former pupils, Leopold and Rainer. The seventeen-year-old Anton too might momentarily be called to the colors. This would leave the Infanta and her remaining children pretty well stranded. Perhaps Pater Gregor's advice ought to be taken after all.

Needless to say, the Archduke Pepi was not consulted in the matter. After some days of maternal indecision his fate had ultimately been decided. He was to set out with Pater Gregor for Feldkirch.

It would be Franz Josef's first journey away from home,

and as such it remained memorable, for he was to be plunged abruptly into a world grown hostile to his kind. In part this hostility was called forth by an error in judgment, caused by Mama's choice of a private railroad compartment for her son. Still thinking in prewar terms, the Infanta had not noticed that social changes made exclusiveness unfashionable. With hunger stalking the streets of Vienna a first-class railroad ticket for a young archduke was a mistake.

As Franz Josef and his tonsured escort closed the door to their compartment, fellow passengers gathered in the passage outside and volubly aired their opinions. Some stooped to peer through the keyhole or the cracks in the drawn blinds, goggling the princelet and the priest. Their audible comments took on an ominous note of anti-clericalism, noticeably on the rise throughout Europe since Russia's negation of Christianity.

"Who's the brat, and the frocked one with him?"

"There you have it! The papist rides in luxury, while working people must stand!"

"Wait till we settle with those clerics and with their wealthy patrons too——"

The boy and his companion caught each angry word, as indeed they were intended to. Franz Josef was both terrified and fascinated. This seemed just like something out of Mama's books: when Marie Antoinette of France had fled with her family by stage coach to Varennes she could hear mutterings and threats along the route of her journey, as could the King and the two children.

Suddenly Franz Josef remembered what had gone wrong with that frantic and almost successful trip. Undetected within the curtained privacy of the carriage, Their Majesties were nearing the border of Alsace, when the little Dauphin announced a minor physiological urge.

"Louis, the chamber pot!" said the Queen to her husband.

His Majesty was a good father. With prompt solicitude he located the needed receptacle, kept handily atop a mound of baggage. But the carriage being crowded, and in any case to lend dignity to the matter, he signaled the coachman to halt, and stepped out with his son.

Here was the error that led to the guillotine. A passing peasant recognized the King, busily unbuttoning the Dauphin's breeches. Furtively the man raced across the fields and took a short cut to the next town, where he gave the alarm. By the time the lumbering coach approached with its royal burden there was a mob armed with pickaxes, scythes and flails, barricading the road.

Yes, the Archduke Pepi knew the story quite well. He recalled Mama's emphasis on the ludicrous crux of the Bourbon disaster. "One must have self-control," Mama had summed up the moral to be drawn from the abortive flight to Varennes.

It was a moral to be heeded on this present and none too comfortable journey to Feldkirch. What with uncertain train schedules the ride would last many hours. But Pater Gregor and his ward had resolved to remain silently in their compartment. They would not brave the congested passageway for any purpose whatsoever.

"Not even," Franz Josef promised in manly tones, "for a walk to the washroom!"

No matter how long the trip, they meant to sit it out.

Chapter Four

On reaching the Boys' Academy of Stella Matutina, the Archduke Pepi was parted from his tutor. He was also parted from his beloved nickname, for the Jesuit school observed strictest formality between teachers and students.

Stella Matutina had long been a famous institution which drew into its halls the sons of dynastic and titled families from every corner in Europe. At present its attendance was sharply restricted by the war, as no French, Belgian, Polish, Russian or Balkan children were enrolled. The pupils were chiefly Austrian and German, with a sprinkling of Italians who had been unable to return home when their country ended its vacillations and joined the Entente against the Central Powers. For this default on the part of a former ally the Italian-born elements at the school were made to suffer. Austrian students combined against them and indulged in harsh vilifications.

On the other hand the Austrian lads themselves had to endure mistreatment by the Germans, for the course of the war had created tension between Berlin and Vienna. Prussian prowess was not matched on the Danube: the Kaiser regarded Habsburg armies as poor stuff. This fact was known even to schoolboys at Stella Matutina. Accordingly the students of Teutonic origin expressed their contempt, not by the innocuous device of name-calling, but by sound thrashings administered to Italians and Austrians alike.

For Franz Josef, so long the coddled Benjamin at home, these feuds were terrifying beyond words. He had never been struck in his life, a fact for which the Jesuit school would amply make up. There seemed to be no higher board of justice to which one might appeal for help, since faculty members themselves were in a difficult position with regard to the school bullies. There had of late been alarming rumors issuing from Berlin to the effect that Germany's General Staff must eventually take over control of incompetent Austria, in which case disciplinarian measures againt Teutonic charges at the Feldkirch Academy would most certainly have brought upon clerical heads the age-old accusation of playing politics. It was because of this that the Jesuit brethren painstakingly ignored outbreaks of violence among students.

Needless to say, this policy made matters especially hard for the newly arrived Franz Josef. Almost from the start, as soon as his identity became known, he was taunted with the Emperor Karl's abortive peace negotiations in London and Paris. These "underhanded" efforts to stop the European carnage had earned the young monarch a withering dressing-down from the Kaiser.

But what had the child Franz Josef to do with all this? His relationship to the Emperor Karl was so remote (a fifth cousinship, to be exact) that they were not even acquainted. And in any case, the sovereign's action ought in no way to reflect upon the character of a small boy.

Misery not only wants company, but soon finds it. Enrolled in Franz Josef's class was a swarthy, somewhat puny lad, Prince Gaetano of Bourbon-Parma, youngest brother of Austria's dethroned Empress Zita. Though this "in-law" relationship to the Viennese court constituted no actual Habsburg blood ties, Franz Josef was happy to find Gaetano. But he rejoiced even more at sight of two first cousins, the Archdukes Clemens and Theodor, sons of Franz Salvator, Papa's brother, and the Archduchess Valerie. Aunt Valerie and Aunt Gisela, as everyone knew, had been the daughters of beautiful Empress Elisabeth, and sisters to that Crown Prince Rudolf who had died at Mayerling.

It was good to see Clemens and Theodor, though of course their presence could scarcely be of any help. Together with Franz Josef and Gaetano they were made the butt of countless pranks and humiliations. Their combined plight grew particularly agonizing when one of the quartet received a package from home.

"Share! Share! Share!" went up the cry from an assembled student body.

Woe to the child who did not surrender his property that instant. Like a wolf pack the others hurled themselves upon him, beating him up and tearing the package to bits. It was part of the hysteria of war and the constant nagging hunger that made the school a world in miniature, where children instead of adults were at one another's throats. That savage shriek of "Share! Share! Share!" was the fundamental germ of Bolshevism, dormant in the human breast at all times, and given impetus through recent events in Russia. Its manifestation at Stella Matutina did not make a lovely picture.

Actually the growing scarcity of foodstuffs had begun to tell on the teaching staff as well. The Infanta Blanca had been right in doubting that the Jesuit Fathers could last very long as experimental farmers. Though trained in asceticism, the monks at Stella Matutina were overworked almost beyond physical endurance. For them, as for worldlier men, the war was lasting too long. With the mounting strain the renowned Jesuit composure cracked here and there on ever weaker pretext.

During history class one day the children were to witness an upsetting display of adult war nerves. Due to the shortage of instructors, particularly during plowing time, upper and lower grades had to be taught in unison by the same teacher, in this case by a stocky and irascible pedant, Father Johannes. The task would have been difficult for any pedagogue, since it required simultaneous adjustment to an audience in part adolescent and in part infantile. Father Johannes, a pronounced neurotic, was not equal to it.

He addressed himself from the outset to the older boys, expounding to them the seafaring propensities of the early Phoenicians. But his heart was not in his work, for only that morning news had come of a general Austrian retreat along the Piave. This was not all. As a further blow to national pride, Army Headquarters had just revealed that last year's great victory at Caporetto, where some 300,000 Italians had been taken prisoner (10,000 dead, 30,000 wounded), had not been won by the Emperor Karl's forces at all. By official admission the 14th German Army under command of General von Below, already in decisive action on the Isonzo, had donned Austrian uniforms and turned the tide at Cividale, Udine, and Caporetto itself. To be told that Austria's greatest battle had been claimed as a German success was more than even a noncombatant Jesuit could bear. Here was degradation indeed.

Suddenly Father Johannes forgot about the early Phoenicians, as the stress of the hour outweighed even the most glorious exploits of vanished antiquity. One fact alone stood out in his mind: Austria and her sister states should never have entered this war.

Staring at the class, his gaze chanced to fix on the archducal children. An unaccountable rage against the very name of Habsburg seized him.

"*They* are at fault!" he snarled. "Their stubborn uncle had to go to Bosnia and get murdered——"

He paused for breath, then noticed the quavering Gaetano

Archduke Leopold Salvator as a young man.

Archduke Leopold Salvator and his bride, the Infanta Blanca.

of Bourbon-Parma. "And that one's sister is even worse."
The diatribe was directed now at Zita. "The morale of our
armies has been undermined by her intrigues for a separate
peace!"

This was the signal for a general uproar. Within a matter
of seconds the classroom was turned into a boxing ring,
where, needless to say, the royal children drew the worst.

That night the young Franz Josef, nursing an assortment
of bruises, wrote a cautious letter to his mother. The school
was very good, he said, and he had made friends with many
of the boys. Now came the part that must get past the prior's
censorship: would Mama please send for him so he could
spend Christmas at home?

The Infanta studied this missive and read between the
lines. There was no doubt about it; her young son was unhappy. But these were times when people everywhere must
acquaint themselves with sorrow. Only the strong survived;
the weak must perish.

She wrote a Spartan answer, admonishing Franz Josef; he
was a very lucky boy. With no one at home to teach him,
did he want to miss school and become an uneducated boor?
As for Christmas, she did not know where any of them
would be by that time. He had best remain right where he
was, in the hands of the good Jesuit Fathers. And a parting
warning: he must never be a snob, abusing less privileged
children by lording it over them. She did not want a bully
for a son.

In his hapless predicament Franz Josef was unable to ap-
preciate the humor of that last line. Under prevailing conditions at the Academy of Stella Matutina nothing was more
unlikely than the Infanta's acquisition of a "bully for a son."

But what worried Franz Josef most about Mama's letter
was her comment on Christmas. What did she mean, not

knowing where any of them would be by that time? Could anything be more important than Christmas, unless perhaps it was one's own Saint's Day? So passionately did Franz Josef love these holidays with their gratifying accompaniment of sweets and presents that, as a very small lad, he had gone about reminding people—even if, by the calendar, such dates might still be quite far off. He had once received a toy wagon piled high with gifts, which he never forgot. Thereafter, at frequent intervals, he drew the empty wagon behind him as a kind of hint, while he made his rounds among older brothers, sisters, and benevolent uncles or aunts. He addressed them all (this being during his toddling days, when he still spoke baby talk) with the same set speech:

"*Vat Du gibst Du tu mein Fest?*" This might be approximately in equally bad English: "Vat you give you to my feast?"

Whereat he was laughingly rebuffed: "*Nix Du kriegst Du tu Dein Fest!*" ("Nix you get you to your feast!")

Yet in the end, when finally the longed-for yuletide or birthday arrived, he had been showered with enchanting surprises, just as were his brothers and sisters in their turn.

Was all this now to stop? He realized for the first time that, as it impinged upon his own personal fate, war was calamitous indeed. He began to grasp what people meant when they said that the whole world had become unhinged. A world that could forget about Christmas was certainly in a bad way.

Just how bad, he had only begun to discover. It was during Franz Josef's eighth week at boarding school that the Austro-Hungarian armies were ordered to lay down their arms on the long front from Asiago to Padua. This preliminary cessation of hostilities would be followed nine days later by the formulation of a general armistice.

The effect upon Stella Matutina paralleled that on the home front everywhere. Returning troops, discharged from service, were suddenly on the loose, uncertain which way to turn. All discipline relaxed as people foraged for themselves, breaking into military stores and falling upon the last reserves of fuel, clothing and foodstuffs.

At Feldkirch the Jesuit Fathers found their own cache of provender rifled by marauders, who left the shelves bare of everything save a stock of carrots. In traditional student fashion the resident pupils had often groused about school menus, referring to Saturday's hash as *"Elefantendreck"* ("elephant dung") or a singularly stringy and uninviting horsemeat stew as *"Jesuitengedärme"* ("Jesuit guts"). Despite such villainous slander, these dishes were nutritive and vastly superior to the thin porridge that graced the average table. Only after the friars disbanded and the school was closed, because of the impossibility to get even a stick of kindling wood, did departing students think with longing of the bill of fare they once had mocked.

For the unbelievable happened, as though in answer to Franz Josef's fervent prayers. The Stella Matutina, established more than a century before, was obliged to shut its doors. Overnight the boys' families were notified that a lay brother would accompany the children as far as Vienna where, it was hoped, their respective relatives or guardians would be on hand to meet them.

There were yet, Franz Josef reflected joyfully, almost seven days till Christmas.

Chapter Five

STEPANEK WAS AT THE STATION, but no sign of Mama or any other members of the family. Franz Josef looked about in puzzled bewilderment. To right and left of him boys ran into the arms of waiting mothers, fathers, or seemingly doting guardians, yet for him there was only Stepanek—the tutor of small Carlos.

Franz Josef's sensitivity, never far below the surface, was sharply stirred. Again the realization struck him that he was no longer the Benjamin, else could he have been so overlooked? If it were Carlos who came home alone at two o'clock in the morning (the train was five hours late) would Carlos have been met only by Stepanek?

Tears welled up into the large blue eyes, but he swallowed them bravely. He must not show how deeply he was hurt.

"*Grüss' Gott, Herr Stepanek,*" he greeted the frock-coated tutor.

"Good day, Your Highness!"

He wanted to ask about Mama, hoping against hope that she might be sitting in her carriage outside the station. But if that were so, Marko, the coachman, would be here to carry the baggage. Franz Josef looked around. No Marko. And, for that matter, no baggage. At the far end of the train a commotion must be brewing, for there was the sound of baffled and angry voices.

"The express car has been robbed! There's not a piece of baggage——"

In another moment pandemonium reigned on the station platform as schoolboys, relatives, gatemen and porters milled about the empty baggage car. But their shouts and gesticulations were in vain; not a single duffel bag remained in sight.

For the Archduke Pepi (here in Vienna the nickname seemed to associate itself once more with him) the loss of mere property was tempered by the spiritual setback he had suffered. What was a trunk, when you yourself had been forgotten? Besides, he reflected in more practical terms, under his arm he carried his toiletries case with nightshirt, clothes brush, and other grooming paraphernalia. Disdainfully he turned his back upon the rifled baggage car.

"Let's go home," he said to Stepanek.

It was at this point that the blow fell. "Your Highness—" the tutor paused to clear his throat—"we cannot go—er —home; that is, to the Galitzin Hill——"

The child did not comprehend. "Of course we can. Mama is waiting!"

Stepanek shook his head. "Your Highness must come to my house in town, not far from here, a little flat in the Tenth District——"

"But why?"

Again something was wrong with Stepanek's throat, for he engaged in a prolonged coughing spell. At last, between barks, the truth emerged:

"There's trouble at Wilhelminenberg."

"Trouble?" Franz Josef was almost glad. Then he had *not* been forgotten! Something had happened—something important, even serious—to keep Mama and the others from meeting him! His face brightened. A smile replaced the childish pout. How silly of him to think that he was not loved!

"There's a mob marching on your father's castle," Stepanek's voice cut into these reveries. "Her Highness and your brothers and sisters are scattered in different hiding places all over town."

Franz Josef stared in sudden terror. "Hiding? Where? Take me to them!" He clutched Stepanek's hand, vainly coaxing the tutor into a run.

"That is impossible. My instructions are to take you to my flat where someone will call for you before morning."

"Someone? Who?"

"His Imperial Highness, Leopold Salvator——"

"Papa? Nonsense! Papa is at the front in Italy!"

Stepanek propelled the boy to a fiacre, waiting at the curb. "Are you forgetting that the war is over?"

"But my brothers, Leopold and Rainer, they are fighting on the Piave——"

"There's no more fighting on the Piave. Your brothers have come back, with buttons and insignia torn from their uniforms. There's not an officer left with epaulettes on his shoulders. This is the Revolution! No man in soldier's garb can show his face——"

The boy listened, as though this were but a twice-told tale. Here it was again: the unbroken thread that ran through those unforgotten reading periods in Mama's sitting room. The streets of Paris under the Commune. Versailles surrounded by armed mobs.

"The Emperor and Empress," Franz Josef asked, and for a moment his voice seemed that of an adult, "are they at Schönbrunn?"

"There is no Emperor or Empress. On November twelfth, the day after the Armistice, the Communists took over and proclaimed Austria a republic. The imperial colors, black and gold, are abolished, as are all titles of nobility and military rank." For an instant Stepanek's face relaxed into a sardonic grin. "Under the New Order, Your Highness would be called Comrade Pepi——"

In the darkness of the cab one could not see the child's

reaction. There was no change in the sound of Franz Josef's voice as he asked again:

"Where are Their Majesties?"

The tutor's report became factual once more. "The Emperor Karl signed the abdication on November thirteenth, though he did not renounce his claim to the Hungarian throne. In Budapest he is still King."

"Why?"

"The Hungarians did not ask him to abdicate. They have been a monarchy for a thousand years—longer than any nation in Europe. It follows that they are content with kings."

"Then Their Majesties have gone to Budapest?"

"No, they are at Schönbrunn with the children, under guard, while a commission headed by delegates of the Allies decides where they will be sent."

The tutor fell silent and for the rest of the ride there was no sound beyond the *clop-clop* of the fiacre's lean nag. At length the carriage came to a stop at Number 30, Buchsbaumgasse, where Stepanek's aged father kept a flat, paid for by his son.

Still without speaking, the royal child and his companion groped their way through the dark vestibule and up four flights of stairs. At the top Papa Stepanek, a wizened octogenarian with a long Biblical beard, awaited them, lantern in hand.

"*Mein Gott,* but you are late," complained the ancient one. "Already I feared something had happened——"

He lighted the way into the tiny apartment, setting the lamp on a table. Its rays fell across a corner cabinet which Franz Josef recognized, for it came from Castle Wilhelminenberg's vast collection of rococo pieces. His parents were in the habit of giving away furniture, however costly or historic, which they could spare. So long as the recipients were

Austrian, they argued, the national treasure was not diminished. An heirloom from the days of the great Empress Maria Theresia was as certain of reverence and loving care at the Stepaneks' as though it were stored in the hushed refuge of the Vienna Museum.

"Sit down, child," said Papa Stepanek, propping up pillows in a huge armchair. Then to his son: "There's milk on the stove, Karl—half a liter. I got it from Frau Bandl, downstairs."

And then it was not long before the Archduke Pepi found himself tucked into a high feather bed, with curtains all around and a crucifix at its head.

"We'll lock the door," the Stepaneks explained before retiring to a makeshift couch in the living room, "in case there's a disturbance during the night."

There *was* a disturbance during the night, though not of the sort father and son had in mind. No bloodthirsty Reds broke into the house to track down fugitive aristocrats. But the Archduke Pepi, locked up in the stuffy little room, became violently ill. Whether it was caused by the night's excitement or by the awesome strangeness of that patriarchal bed—or simply by the fact that half a liter of milk at one gulp had been too much for his small stomach—the boy's insides turned over.

He looked about in dismay. Where was the bathroom in this unfamiliar place? Should he call the Stepaneks, senior or junior?

Embarrassment and a sense of delicacy restrained him. Not only was it humiliating to broadcast a physical need, but he did not want to pain his hosts by vomiting their priceless milk. Still, vomit he must. It was imperative to find the bathroom.

In the midst of his agony the dreadful truth finally

dawned. From confidential chatter with servants on Galitzin Hill he remembered that only "people of means" and
royalty, of course, had bathrooms, while lesser mortals—like
the Stepaneks—shared a key to some obscure little retreat
that served an entire community of apartment-house lodgers.
In fact, wasn't this what seemed to be wrong with royalty
and "people of means" in general? Or rather, did the evil
lie not so much in the circumstance that the privileged few
possessed such a multitude of good things, as that the underprivileged multitudes possessed so little?

Well, this was no time to settle academic questions. The
Archduke Pepi must find relief, and he must find it in a
hurry. Without further ado he leaped to the window,
opened it, and leaned over the ivy-covered ledge. A nice
little plum tree stood directly below. That was too bad.

In scarcely two seconds it was all over, and he felt instantly better. Only now, on reviewing the crisis, did his
gaze meet the black walnut night table with the customary
little door beneath it. There it had sat reassuringly beside
the bed all the time, discreetly harboring that vessel so indispensable in the absence of plumbing. Out of sheer happiness he lifted it out and used it too.

Before seven o'clock in the morning there was loud
knocking on his door. Still drowsy with sleep, Franz Josef
heard his brother Anton's voice:

"Hurry up, Pepi! I've come to take you to the station."

To the station? The boy was flabbergasted. Hadn't he
and Stepanek just come from there last night?

He dressed hastily after washing in a bowl of ice-cold
water; the rationing of fuel (and its ultimate disappearance
for anything but cooking) had long ago put an end to the
pleasure of cleansing oneself beyond a few perfunctory
splashes. While Pepi ran a comb through his unruly hair,

which always curled abominably when wet, Anton explained the events of the past few weeks.

The Republic, it appeared, had no further use for Habsburgs, and was readying a decree enforcing their banishment unless they agreed to renounce their titles. As a result the Emperor Karl, before signing his own abdication, had given notice to all male members of the family that they were henceforth on their own. They could toss overboard the priceless heritage and high honor earned by their ancestors, so as to curry favor with an upstart and untried regime. Or —and the monarch left no doubt where lay his own preference—they could go into exile. If they chose the latter, His Majesty recommended that they get out before being kicked out.

It was a harsh and irreverent alternative, dictated by harsh and irreverent times. But the House of Habsburg had weathered storms before. It must take this one in its stride. All over Austria the archdukes were packing.

Departure would not be so easy as at first anticipated. The populace of Vienna, good-natured and jovial in normal times, wore suddenly a different face. The doctrines of Trotzky and Lenin had taken effect beyond Russian borders, and Habsburgs appeared at the moment as unpopular as Romanovs.

In view of this it was advisable to make as little commotion as possible. How could a large household like that of Leopold Salvator, with ten children and even a minimum of baggage, get under way without commotion? Obviously by splitting up into several groups.

Mama, putting on widow's weeds and calling herself Madame Blanche Navarre, took small Carlos and went off with him to her friend, Señora López, wife of the Chilean Ambassador. Since Fräulein Kurtz, the governess, had long ago elected to return to her German kin at Mainz, the young archduchesses were placed in the care of their mother's Spanish lady-in-waiting, Asunción Correa, whose connections gave them access to the Peruvian Legation.

The older boys must fend for themselves, keeping in hiding until the prearranged signal summoned them all to a secret point of departure. They left Wilhelminenberg during the night, climbing over the gates while the watchman drowsed on his beat.

There was still the problem of Papa, whose high military rank had for years made him the target of news cameras throughout the land. His face was as familiar to the man in the street as that of Frau Sacher, the famous restaurant hostess.

Actually Papa had been enormously popular. But in times of revolution personal appeal is nullified by class distinctions and class hatreds. The greatly esteemed artillery commander was a member of the dethroned dynasty and, as such, an enemy of the new state. Russia had dispersed or slaughtered her blue bloods. It was now open season on Habsburgs along the Danube.

The first thing for Papa to do was to put on disguise. He had already exchanged his uniform for mufti, but though a fedora altered his appearance, any child playing along the avenues of the Prater would have recognized him.

"I do believe, dear," said Madame Navarre, "that you must grow a beard."

He not only raised a magnificent hirsute screen that curtained the whole lower part of his face, but he was to sally forth from his castle as Don Giuseppe d'Aquila, a bachelor of Florentine antecedents. Since Italy was now a victor nation, no harm could come to one with such a name. (A student of psychology might well compute the high degree attached by a Habsburg to his house, if he regarded the prefix "Don" and the apostrophe of nobility as a concession to the great leveler, Democracy. By becoming the Italian equivalent of a Spanish grandee an archduke had come down in the world.)

At the last moment someone had remembered young Franz Josef. What was to be done about the lad, immured in the Jesuit privacy of Stella Matutina? To send a messenger was hazardous, as it would endanger the secrecy of the plan of flight. Besides, the special refugee train promised by the mayor of Vienna, Bürgermeister Breitner, might be ready at any moment. There was actually no time to fetch the boy. Indeed, was he not better off—and safer than all the rest—with the good monks of Feldkirch? Yes, they had better leave Pepi behind.

It was pure chance that the Jesuit Fathers had decided at this precise moment to close their school. Had they done so but one day later Franz Josef would have stood penniless and abandoned at the Westbahnhof in Vienna. Robbed of his trunk, he would have faced the future with a tiny satchel holding his toilet articles and a nightshirt that could do with some laundering. Not even Stepanek would have been there to meet him. For, with everyone gone from Galitzin Hill, the message from the school would have remained undelivered.

It was an appalling thought. While his brother Anton recited these things in the Stepaneks' cramped sitting room Franz Josef knew suddenly just what it must be like to be an orphan.

Chapter Six

THERE WERE, ACCORDING TO ANTON, unexpected complications with old Resi, the nursemaid.

Resi disapproved of what was going on. She disapproved, in fact, of the course that history was taking. At the very moment that her employers made ready to move out of Wilhelminenberg, Resi had wrapped her polishing cloths about both feet and was giving the nursery floor a good going over. She did this by moving gingerly back and forth in a skating pattern over the waxed surface.

"But Resi," someone explained, "that isn't necessary any more——"

The old woman gave a snort. As if she would let her baby Carlos sleep in a dusty room! The "baby" Carlos happened to be eight years old and most resentful of such ministrations. He tried to make her understand:

"I won't be sleeping here after today. Mama is taking me to visit Coco and Nando (Fernando) Pérez, and from there we are going far away."

Resi couldn't stand it. Breaking into great sobs, she wandered off to the kitchens in search of some flour scrapings, a few dried-up currants and some ersatz egg, to make a *Stritzl*. At least, if her loved masters had to brave the world, she would see to it that they took along a cake. But for her own precious Carlos she had something special: a hoard of prewar rock candy, strung on a bit of twine and reposing in a tiny box under the floor boards of Resi's room. Everyone suffered from deficiency diseases nowadays, particularly loss of energy because there was no sugar. Well, the Archduke Carlos, fortified with Resi's rock candy, would have better resistance than most.

Having disposed of her hidden treasure, the old nurse turned back to her cleaning. Even if they all went off and left her, the gendarmes taking over the castle would find Resi armed with cloth and a bottle of polish, rubbing door-knobs and brass lintels to a fine sheen.

It was at this stage that the eldest of the boys, Archduke Rainer, had decided suddenly to remain behind. He would drop his title and swear allegiance to the new Republic. As a simple Herr Habsburg he intended to find a job, for he had considerable mechanical ability which had led him to study the watchmaker's art for a hobby. Besides, from early childhood Rainer had chosen for himself a motto which he translated into faulty (if Classic) Greek:

"Euka di men e bei beltion estion!"

Roughly translated, this meant that it was better to stay home than to travel. Years ago Rainer used to recite this motto whenever the family made ready to go away on sum-mer holidays; he much preferred to be left behind so he could tinker with his bicycle.

"It's *beltion estion* with Rainer again," said the other children, resigned to their elder brother's idiosyncrasy.

Today, however, the situation was more serious. Papa and Mama wanted to make sure that Rainer understood the long-range consequences of his choice.

"You know of course what this means?" they warned. "If there should one day be a restoration, you can never again be an imperial prince——"

The young man nodded. He had barely come of age, but there was upon him the weariness of all who had served too long in the trenches.

"Personally," he said, "I don't expect to see a restoration."

On this note he and the family had parted.

Rainer's decision did not go unnoticed by his next younger brother, Archduke Leopold. In fact, it threw Leopold into a spiritual conflict, as he was deeply in love with a Croatian Baroness Dagmar Nikolitch-Podrinski, cousin of the concert artist Muk de Jari. It was an adolescent romance, frowned upon by the family on the grounds of extreme youth. But Leopold intended to marry Dagmar. To do so he too would have to defy parental objection and remain in Vienna.

Leopold differed from Rainer on one point. What was the sense of changing names and dropping titles? You were born what you were born. Even if you put on a false nose, you were still bone and blood of Holy Roman Emperors. ... He did not care what other people called him, but there was only one thing he could call himself: Archduke of Austria. ...

Like Rainer, of course, he too must look for a job. With wedding bells in mind, he decided to take the first thing that offered itself, namely a position as film carrier for a circuit of Vienna motion-picture theaters. The job entailed rushing from one projection booth to another in some distant neighborhood with reels of the same film which, for reasons of economy, existed in only one print and had to be shown by relay.

Pedaling on a bicycle from theater to theater, Leopold not only saved the continuity of several matinees, running concurrently, but also managed an occasional rendezvous with Dagmar so as to keep his romance afloat. In short, here was a young man one need not worry about.

Yielding parental authority, Papa and Mama turned to a

problem of greater urgency. It was the matter of family finances.

Under the provisional government of Chancellor Dr. Renner and Vice-Chancellor Fink, state funds had been seized and the imperial income cut off. Private Habsburg properties were due next to undergo revision, with expropriation in prospect. This left practically no source of cash, even if cash had had any value during the prevailing inflation.

Fortunately even a collateral archducal line, though remote from the throne, owned family jewels of seemly worth. Diamonds and sapphires were always convertible into food and lodgings, no matter what the political complexion of a land. Of this the Infanta had been quite certain, as she personally sewed her most valuable trinkets—an emerald necklace and an heirloom known as the "Marie Antoinette Brooch"—into a sash, which could be worn under the voluminous folds of her coat. This added girth gave Mama a fecund bulge no longer suited to her age or her masquerading widowhood, but it immeasurably bolstered the family's sense of security. Whenever monetary difficulties arose, the Infanta could shell out a single emerald, or a diamond from the Bourbon brooch. A third gem, the "Diadem of Hortense," was not so easy to conceal. This diamond-studded piece, presented by Napoleon to the daughter of his first wife, Empress Josephine, had been entrusted to Stepanek for safekeeping.

As for the immediate expenses connected with the archducal flight, diplomatic hands had come to the rescue. The representatives of Chile, Argentina, and Peru were rushing their wives and children abroad, hence the private refugee train made available by City Councillor Breitner. A large number of interned Italians had to be repatriated at the

The family.

Standing, left to right: Dolores, Infanta Blanca, Leopold, Immaculata, Margareta, Anton; *sitting, left to right:* Rainer, Assunta, Carlos, Maria Antonia, Archduke Leopold Salvator, Franz Josef.

At Castle Wilhelminenberg.

Left to right: Anton, Franz Josef, Maria Antonia, Margareta, Rainer, Leopold, Immaculata, Dolores, Assunta; *on floor*: Carlos.

same time. The fugitive Habsburgs would simply ride along.

It was to this train that Archduke Anton had now come to fetch his brother Franz Josef. As there was little time to lose, the farewell in the Stepanek parlor was poignant and brief.

"God be with you," said the former tutor, embracing the two lads whom he had taught to read.

"*Servus!*" they answered in the affectionate Viennese vernacular, as they were now in his debt. They also made a courtly bow to Papa Stepanek, who pressed a boiled egg and a sack of prunes into their hands.

"We dried these prunes ourselves," explained both Stepaneks with pardonable pride. "They're from the little plum tree underneath the window!"

For a moment Franz Josef felt he ought to say something about that plum tree. But he thought better of it. Following his brother downstairs, he stepped quickly into the street and turned his back on Buchsbaumgasse 30.

From other parts of town the remaining members of the refugee party made their way toward the railroad yards behind the Central Station. The train waited inconspicuously on a side track.

At the appointed meeting place a surprise awaited everyone as the Infanta, Carlos, and the five young archduchesses arrived in the family limousine driven by Marko, the chauffeur of Galitzin Hill. This was an unpardonable and foolhardy risk for which only the old retainer could be blamed. By general agreement all movement was to be on foot or by public conveyance, so as to attract no attention. But the faithful Marko would not stand for it. Rather than see his employers roam the streets or hail a passing cabby, he had sneaked back to the castle and, under cover of night, made off with the car.

In carrying out this gallant feat Marko was doing nobody a favor save himself, for it was no pleasure to ride with him. An expert coachman, he had for years handled the reins of the family landau, and even the festive glass coach for state occasions at Schönbrunn. But at the wheel of a gasoline-driven *Isotta* or *Austro-Fiat,* the erstwhile groom turned into a menace to himself, his passengers, and traffic at large. Marko disapproved of automobiles. He thought them noisy, inelegant, and slightly plebeian. But his real trouble lay in the fact that he personalized all things, motors included. When the car drove up a particularly steep hill, Marko leaned forward helpfully and rose off his haunches, puffing from exertion. He was also not above coaxing the machine along with whoops and whistles or breaking into a loud cheer when a stretch of hazardous terrain had been negotiated. But worst of all, in the midst of downtown traffic Marko sometimes became unnerved by the exigencies of a machine age. At such moments he threw up both arms in desperation, prayed to Saint Aloysius, who presumably must take over, and for the rest allowed the four wheels to drift whither they would.

With a good team of palfreys, such irresponsible behavior had never led to catastrophe, as the animals were far more intelligent than their unpredictable driver. While Marko hurled curses at some hated tramcar or hack the horses deftly threaded their way through the maze and headed for home.

It was different with automobiles, which had no gift for improvisation. This fact could not seem to penetrate Marko's thick skull. In any case, when the Infanta saw him driving up to convey her to the train she made the sign of the cross.

"If we can just get out of Austria without being killed by Marko," she said fervently, "the rest will be easy!"

Why did she ride with him? Here was a riddle not to be solved unless one understood the very essence of the Viennese character—even, as in the case of the Infanta, that of a Viennese by adoption. Like Bratfisch, the favorite cabby of the ill-fated Archduke Rudolf, Marko had become an institution. Good, bad, or indifferent, the feudal coachman was a fixture to be endured for life. None more devoted to his master than the keeper of the stable; if at the same time he was mildly homicidal, one overlooked such foibles.

The Infanta not only overlooked. She resolutely schooled herself to lean back in the car cushions and take a nap. Only thus could an outing with Marko be borne.

Still napping, she arrived now with Carlos and her daughters at the railroad yards. The others had already assembled. There was Papa looking like Rasputin in his beard. He had added green goggles to his disguise, which gave him an owlish appearance.

Besides the archducal family, there was the personnel of the Chilean diplomatic household as well as a flock of legation children. Among the latter, Franz Josef spotted his particular cronies, Enrique and Gigi (Eugenio) López, with their sister Rita and a baby brother still in his pram. Enrique was athletic and great fun at hockey or even ping pong. Gigi had no talents at all, unless one made mention of his prodigious appetite. Gigi was always hungry. Not only that, he had an extraordinary knack for finding food, often in the most unlikely places, which made him highly appreciated as a playmate. Wherever Gigi went one could be sure of provender.

After a careful roll call, the travelers were divided into several groups and assigned to their places on the train. Only now did it become evident that all available passenger vehicles had been reserved for the Italian repatriates, while the "Refugee Special" provided by the Vienna *Stadtrat* consisted of two cattle cars attached to the main convoy. It appeared furthermore that these cars had seen war service and most likely had been converted by the Red Cross for transportation of the wounded. They were equipped with bunks still soiled and blood-spattered from use. After the Armistice no one had bothered to clean out these discarded vehicles. What for? Defeated Austria was done for a while with traveling.

Accommodations in the boxcars were allocated now strictly according to age: older people, less able to withstand discomfort, entered the Red Cross *wagon lits,* while the children and servants did without bunks. Luckily everyone had brought along at least one blanket, in compliance with the first rule for a successful refugee: *Keep warm!* Food and water are of no use after one is dead from freezing.

A commissary was formed by pooling all available edibles, to be rationed as needed. The South Americans supplied by far the greater portion of canned goods, sardines, pickled meats, and some rare cinnamon-flavored chocolate, received in occasional shipments from their countries overseas. But the archducal family too contributed its mite: there were several loaves of black bread, some jars of superannuated marmalade carefully hoarded against just such a day as this, and lastly, Resi's farewell *Stritzl*. True, this latter had been baked for Resi's special pet, the little Carlos, but in the present circumstances private property had been abolished.

"As far as eating is concerned," the Archduke Leopold Salvator declared, "we are all Communists. Every crumb must be shared."

He also forbade the children to address him as their father. If asked, they must say that he was their Uncle Giuseppe.

For Franz Josef, free from the rigors of his Jesuit school, all this was quite a lark. For one thing, he had been assigned—with Enrique, Gigi, Rita, and his own brothers and sisters—to the smaller of the cattle cars, heated by a cozy wood stove. It may be that the conveyance at one time had harbored a cargo of goats, for there was a reminiscent odor. But what made matters particularly congenial was the presence of the López manservant, charged with looking after the children's needs. This swarthy individual jabbered incessantly in his native Araucanian dialect or broke into song, much to the delight of his youthful listeners.

The stove proved vitally important as a heating unit no less than as a makeshift kitchen where the travelers could prepare their meals.

This brought up the problem of fuel. There were no more than half a dozen sticks in the wood box beside the stove, while the second cattle car did not even have a brazier. Papa luckily noticed this before the train started, whereupon everyone scurried about the station yards in search of combustible material. The result was skimpy at best, since Vienna citizens in the past four years had learned to pick up every scrap of kindling paper. Only rotted twigs and splinterings seemed to be left.

It was decreed that someone must watch the fire day and night, so as to practice the greatest economy with the available faggots.

"Wood should be added *zitzerlweise* (a tittle at a time)," explained Mama.

At last everything was ready. Bundles and passengers had been stowed aboard, while the locomotive worked up steam. An air of expectancy hovered over the scene, compounded of hopefulness and melancholy.

It was now that, puffing up the station ramp, a breathless and gesticulating figure came into view. It was Karl Stepanek, the tutor.

"Your Highnesses," he exclaimed, rushing up to his former employers, "they are sacking Wilhelminenberg!"

"Not so loud, Stepanek!" warned the startled listeners. "We are traveling incognito! And whom do you mean by *they?*"

The tutor's voice was lowered to a whisper. "Not the townspeople or the rabble, Your High—I mean, Signor d'Aquila, but that scoundrel Schmautzer, your equerry!"

"Schmautzer? Impossible! He's been game warden for thirty years, and well paid, too——"

It nevertheless *was* possible according to Stepanek's account. At this very moment the hawk-faced Schmautzer, still wearing his livery of huntsman's green, was cleaning out the castle. Already he had made off with the contents of the trophy room, selling silver and gold cups to a jeweler in the Kärntnergasse, while the entire collection of antlers had been contracted for by a button factory. The game warden, it appeared, was an excellent businessman.

"He is now emptying the wine cellars," continued Stepanek, "piling bottles into the children's gocart and driving off with Hansl."

Hansl was the old donkey belonging since infancy to the young archdukes and archduchesses. Sheer senility had long ago earned Hansl the comforts of a pensioner's life, for he was now too feeble to pull even small Carlos around the garden paths. Not that in his heyday Hansl had been much of a prize, either for dray purposes or as a mount; he had never been very bright, but on his fuzzy back the children had overcome their first riding fears. At such times Hansl's most conspicuous trick had been an uncanny ability to turn around in a perfect circle and then head for home; no matter where he started from, he never missed the stable.

The idea of the veteran donkey being put to work by an infamous thief aroused even greater consternation than the plundering of the castle itself. Hansl might have a heart attack! He never did like going uphill. Whenever the terrain bothered him and the going got hard, Hansl was accustomed to consideration, as the children had always jumped from the gocart and pushed him gently by his haunches. Would that evil Schmautzer think of this? Not likely.

"If I could only have a signature or something like a power of attorney," muttered Stepanek, "then I could go to the police and apply for a guard."

"You shall have such power," decided Signor d'Aquila.

Turning to his Latin-American friends, he obtained an array of ambassadorial signatures. Armed with a diplomatic petition, Stepanek was to seek official protection for the castle, as well as adequate respect for Hansl's rights.

Only now could the travelers continue on their dubious way.

Chapter Seven

THE TRAIN HEADED FOR TRIESTE, 367 miles southwest of Vienna. In normal times this distance was traversed in seven hours. But today, even though peace had been declared, times were far from normal—the Trieste journey took eight and a half days.

In part the tempo of the trip was dictated by a defective engine, which broke down at regular intervals and called for makeshift repairs. But even when things went well for a stretch, and the little locomotive chugged bravely along, trouble arose: the train personnel (a mere skeleton crew) went suddenly on strike. From engineer to brakeman, all hands declared themselves dissatisfied with working conditions. They thought they would turn back. They were underpaid. The Trieste trip was not really worth their while.

Each time a crisis of this nature arose there were quick conferences held by the worried travelers. From the combined pool of food and funds a donation was made to appease the railroaders. This lasted for the next twenty-five kilometers, and then the operation had to be repeated, until at one point young Archduke Anton took an inspired step. The seventeen-year-old lad had studied engineering in Vienna. Though he knew only the rudiments of train mechanics, Anton jumped into the locomotive cab and turned on the steam.

This unprecedented action aroused first anger, then admiration, from the crew. A schoolboy who could run a train? It was unbelievable! They ought to cut his head off for obstructing the interests of labor. Still, this impertinent stranger knew how to operate a locomotive. Did that not put him on the side of labor? A man who could use his hands—was he not one of them?

This time the trainmen held a conference, to which Anton was asked. After earnest confabulation a truce was arrived at, insuring unbroken progress, save for bona fide engine trouble, during the remainder of the journey. To clinch this new accord, it was decided that the crew might join passengers during mealtimes, provided of course that their own provender was added to the common pool. Since the trainmen's supplies were on the whole more ample and nutritive, the archducal party profited greatly by the arrangement.

The above triumph did not exhaust Anton's resourcefulness. On the third day out it had dawned upon him that this was Christmas Week, with the Holy Night just ahead. Were they to spend this most sacred feast of the year in prosaic flight, without pausing for even a moment's celebration?

He went back to his friends, the trainmen. With so many small children aboard, he argued, ought they not to make some sort of gesture? Even as he talked his eyes scanned the snow-covered landscape.

"Look! Pine forests all around; I could get off and cut down a tree——"

The engineer shook his head. He had just got his locomotive going after a particularly bad breakdown. It would stop of its own accord soon enough; there was no point in courting trouble.

"Oh, you won't have to stop," Anton assured him. "At the rate you're going I can cut a tree and catch up with the last car, not even breaking into a run."

The engineer was a trifle peeved at this. But, as if to rob

him of an answer, the locomotive gave a few asthmatic gasps and slowed down to a crawl. Armed with the fireman's ax, Anton stepped from the tender and made for the woods. He raced forward and picked a young balsam considerably ahead of the train, so as to allow for time lost in chopping. He swung his ax with hard, sure strokes, concentrating on his aim. The important thing was to shoulder his burden with the utmost speed: trees could not run but he, Anton, could.

Through porthole openings in the boxcars a fascinated audience looked on. There were shouts and admonitions from the men, telling Anton just what he must do. Children cheered and clapped their hands, while the women suffered palpitations. But in the end the feat had been accomplished and Anton climbed aboard, trophy in hand.

It was a handsome tree, some six feet high, exactly right for the children's boxcar. A chorus of questions now arose:

"Have we enough candles? What shall we use for trimmings?"

Anton had solved this problem, too, long before cutting down the tree. There were some apples and nuts, as well as Resi's rock candy, already strung on twine. A bit of twisted wire would make candle holders for such tapers as could be spared for one night of luxurious brilliance. Then, for a touch of color, the smaller girls would lend their hair ribbons for garlands.

It all worked out extraordinarily well, even though, of course, there were no presents. As the refugee train rolled on bumpily through darkness, the tree shone brightly and the children's voices piped:

"Stille Nacht, Heilige Nacht . . ."

After the celebration everyone retired, with only the

Chilean manservant Gerónimo staying awake to tend the potbellied stove and the makeshift braziers in the other cars.

On the following day a council of elders was held. Soon the train would be entering Italian territory and one must prepare for a hostile reception. The diplomatic travelers, to be sure, had nothing to fear, but the name of Habsburg was at the moment an unpopular commodity. Every precaution must be taken to perfect the archducal disguise.

For one thing, Don Giuseppe d'Aquila from now on understood only Italian or Spanish, while the Widow Navarre and her offspring must communicate exclusively in French. Woe to anyone who lapsed into Viennese!

The arrangement was of course quite sensible, but difficult of execution, particularly for the children. Their French and Spanish were of the schoolroom variety, and they spoke no Italian at all. Then there was the ticklish matter of calling Papa "Uncle Giuseppe," which required more presence of mind than ordinarily could be expected, at least of the very young.

By way of compromise the children became awkwardly silent. Rather than address their parents as perfect strangers, they said nothing at all.

The border was crossed at Triglau late that night. Happily the passport revision went off without hitch, due to the predominance of Latin-American visas. The false papers carried by the archducal family aroused no suspicion.

With sighs of relief the passengers returned to their cars and the train made ready to chug on, when there was a sudden loud knocking.

"*Apra súbito!* (Open at once!)" came shrill voices through the wall of the children's car.

With sinking heart Signor d'Aquila pushed the door aside, prepared to face the worst. But the sight that met his eyes was reassuring, for along the railroad tracks stood a gathering of ladies attired in some sort of nursing garb. They represented the Travelers' Aid Society of Triglau and they had come tearing through the night to bring clothes and refreshments to the refugees.

"Coffee!" they cried, holding up lanterns to indicate the spot where they would serve the steaming liquid. "Coffee and bread sticks, *amici!*"

The travelers were touched. They descended rapidly to receive the proffered goodies. But at a signal from the locomotive they scrambled aboard almost at once, carefully balancing paper plates and cups.

It happened that the coffee was excellent, for the Allied countries received supplies from North America. But in Vienna weak substitutes had been in use for so long that the genuine article now tasted unbearably strong and bitter. After one swallow the children wanted to throw theirs away.

"Wait!" exclaimed the older women in chorus. "If you can't drink it you can use it for washing——"

This was even worse. For days the younger element had delighted in the water shortage, which had put a halt to customary ablutions in order to preserve the dwindling supply. To be asked now to dip hands and faces into the hot brown liquid rather nullified the earlier satisfaction of going unwashed. But maternal standpoints were firm; either you drank your coffee or you got cleaned up. There were no two ways about it.

Among the adults, Asunción Correa, the lady-in-waiting, most appreciated a chance to do a bit of cleansing. An abstainer, she carried her cup to the "sleeping car" and went to work on the aging bloodstains that covered the bunks. While she did not accomplish their removal, a general blending of spots made the effect less offensive. This soothed Asunción Correa's somewhat neurotic state of mind, for she inclined to morbidity. In younger years, before her early spinsterishness had set in, the lady-in-waiting had been engaged to a British merchant marine officer who went down with the *Titanic*. Her grief for him was sustained and often picturesque, as she lost no chance to associate the most harmless daily events with always impending death. No matter how mild a thunderstorm, she expected to be struck down by lightning, in anticipation of which she never left the house without donning her best lace-trimmed underwear.

"No telling when one may end up in the morgue," she would say, visualizing herself stretched out on a slab of marble, with clothes in disarray. . . . Whatever the eventuality, Asunción Correa liked to be prepared.

The neglected condition of the refugee train to Trieste had afforded her imagination full play. She scorned the explanation that the Red Cross cars had served for the transport of wounded; hearses on rails, she called them, convinced that the corpses had been piled tier upon tier. In sprinkling her coffee about she was banishing the scent of death.

So relieved was everyone at the prospect of the gloomy lady calming down that even those who might have found their beverage palatable surrendered it for her use. At least the ominous stains could now be ascribed to harmless Java.

To offset the brightening of Asunción's disposition there arose a new fuel crisis. The wood supply was again almost exhausted. Even the Christmas tree had gone up in flames, while the rock-strewn landscape through which the train now passed gave little promise of replenishment.

"Let's burn one of the trunks," proposed Signor d'Aquila with nonchalance.

It was a capital idea. A goodsized wardrobe was emptied and its contents tied into bundles. Next the trunk was hacked to bits and fed grudgingly, piece by piece, to the expiring flames. The ensuing smoke smelled of burned hide and varnish, but a gratifying warmth spread once more through the clammy cars.

At last, after more than a week of travel, the train pulled into Trieste. This Adriatic port, known to Slovenes as "Trst" (from the ancient Roman Tergeste), was situated in the province of Venezia Giulia on the fringe of the Julian Alps. His military duties had brought the Archduke Leopold Salvator on frequent visits to the town, while it was under Austrian rule. People were bound to remember his face. Extra caution was called for.

The most obvious step toward that end was again to scatter the family in different hotels. This was no simple matter, since lodgings must be cheap and in keeping with available funds. It was hardly wise to sacrifice an emerald or a chip off the Marie Antoinette Brooch for needless luxury, since neither Madame Navarre nor Signor d'Aquila felt any certainty regarding their ultimate destination or the manner of getting there.

Adding to their sense of insecurity was the fact that in Trieste the Latin-Americans left the caravan. They embarked for Buenos Aires on a luxury liner already waiting at the pier.

The Austrians bade them a forlorn farewell.

Chapter Eight

THE PLACE WHERE MADAME NAVARRE and the children were finally quartered was called Hotel Transalpini, while Signor d'Aquila retired to a miserable hostel with the confident caption Excelsior. There were no family meetings in public; only an occasional short rendezvous between husband and wife for the plotting of the next step.

Spain was the goal they had decided upon. The question to be solved was how to get there.

While their elders hovered patiently about the wharves, making discreet inquiries about departing freighters (passenger vessels were expensive and too conspicuous), the children caught up on some laundering. This was especially urgent in the case of Franz Josef, who had only one set of underwear to his name.

It cannot be said that these efforts made for improvement. The hotel provided no soap, and the family supply barely sufficed for personal needs. Hence the "laundering" consisted of energetic dousings in cold water, with little if any effect.

After ten days of doubt a ray of light showed itself at last. No ship sailed from Trieste for Spain, but the owner of a fishing barge knew of such sailings from Genoa. One must find a way of getting to Genoa.

Train schedules were looked up and the discovery was now made that Italian railroads had been as badly disrupted by the war as those of Austria or Germany. The only rolling stock carried freight and was therefore unavailable to travelers; without the influence of Latin-American diplomats no "refugee special" loomed in sight.

In very urgent cases, Signor d'Aquila was told, an old private car could be rented out, provided passengers paid for every seat. Did Signor d'Aquila wish to think it over?

He did indeed, for the chartering of such a vehicle would definitely break into the emeralds.

"Well," said Madame Navarre, "we'll need cash in Genoa too, if we hope to get on a boat. This is as good a time as any to part with the first stone."

Despite such cool matter-of-factness, the trip to the jeweler was not easy. The necklace had been in the family for generations without such an indignity befalling it. Nor did the loss of this first fragment augur well for what remained. As the future looked right now, the precious bauble would eventually be chopped into bits and scattered far and wide.

Genoa, however, was reached, and here again the family put up at shabby hotels and resumed inquiries along the water front. As luck would have it, a Spanish freighter called the *Teresa Taya* (of the Taya Transport Line) was due to sail for Barcelona within a week.

"Oh," exclaimed Madame Navarre, who believed in omens, "my favorite saint is the Little Flower, Thérèse de Lisieux! Surely that is a good sign——"

After some dickering they were able to book passage on the 3,000-ton vessel, which had a limited number of cabins. There were other passengers aboard—a helpful factor. Since the staterooms were tiny, the family again divided up into units, with the Widow Navarre and the girls quartered on the top deck, while Uncle Giuseppe and his "nephews" retired to steerage level.

In the end this splitting into groups proved a lifesaver. For, just as the ship was about to weigh anchor, a military commission came aboard. The ship's skipper was summoned.

Grandchildren, nephews and nieces of Emperor Franz Joseph I of Austria at Jubilee Celebration.

Left corner: children of Archduke Leopold Salvator; *center figure:* future Emperor Karl; *right corner:* children of Archduchess Valerie.

Children of Archduke Leopold Salvator at Emperor's Jubilee.
Standing, left to right: Anton, Rainer, Dolores, Assunta; *sitting (center):* Margareta, Maria Antonia, Leopold; *front:* Franz Josef.

"An Austrian archduke, his wife and ten children have escaped," the spokesman announced. "He is a high enemy officer and as such accountable to the tribunal determining war guilt. We have orders to search the boat."

The skipper was at the moment engrossed in catching the eye of a cabaret dancer, mincing up the gangplank and proclaiming loudly that she had signed a contract with the most fashionable night club in Madrid. He waved the commission to go ahead and take its time; while the official investigation proceeded he would engage in some amorous research of his own.

The military police were thorough. They checked passports and faces, scrutinizing each in turn. They counted heads and repeated the count. Luckily the Archdukes Rainer and Leopold had remained behind in Vienna, so that their brothers and sisters added up consistently to the wrong figure.

All went well and the commission was preparing to go ashore when a dreadful thing happened. One of the younger children—it must have been Carlos—sighed with relief and broke out:

"*Now* do we sail, Papa?"

There was a chill silence as the commission stopped in its tracks, faces turned to stone.

"What did the boy say?" asked the spokesman pointedly.

It was the resourceful Anton who came to the rescue. "Oh, he called our uncle *Peppe*—you know, the diminutive for Giuseppe."

The gentlemen of the committee exchanged quizzical glances. But, as if on cue, the younger children crowed loudly:

"*Zio Peppe, Zio Peppe!*" ("Uncle Peppe, Uncle Peppe!")

That seemed to clinch matters. Scratching their pates, the

members of the commission departed. It was dusk when the ship put out to sea, heading straight into a storm.

As soon as the shore line vanished and the waves whipped themselves to ever-mounting height, a grave problem became apparent. The boat did not carry enough cargo; the red Primsoll line was thrust constantly upward into view. This meant that passengers and crew would be hopelessly seasick, as even the best of mariners could not withstand a tossing vessel that was without balance.

The tempest increased during the night and the day that followed until, on the third evening, it reached hurricane proportions. The captain, who had hoped to embark on a romantic courtship, lay groaning in his cabin. Even the ship's radio man was too ill to send an SOS.

Almost the only person still up and about, except for the helmsman and a few stokers below deck, was the Archduke Anton. This imperturbable young man had made it his task to explore the vessel from bow to stern. Fascinated by the mysteries of the Morse code, he had lingered beside the nauseated radio man just as a lengthy message happened to come through.

"Look! Look!" he admonished the listless operator. "It's something important. What does it say?"

The other spelled out mechanically, while Anton helpfully wrote down the text. It was a peremptory order from the authorities at Genoa, bidding the ship return at once to port. Reason: the searching party had just figured out that the archducal family was on board after all, since a checkup with Vienna revealed that the missing Rainer and Leopold had remained in Austria.

"Take it to the captain," the radio man begged feebly as he pointed to the message in Anton's hand.

The latter paused. Had the man not grasped the import

of the words spelled out before him? Obviously he did not suspect Anton's identity. What to do? Could there be a better chance than this to throw the message overboard and escape detection?

Anton had a reputation for resourcefulness. But this was different. This called for suppression of an official order issued by the authorities of a country not his own. As a member of a ruling dynasty he might at one time—even though he was still a minor—have held up an Austrian dispatch that ran against his family's interest. But aboard a foreign ship, which was tantamount to foreign soil, such action would be inadmissible.

He did not struggle with his conscience. Stepping out on deck, he walked resolutely to the captain's bridge.

Outside the storm was subsiding. With the dying breeze the sea calmed down to almost uncanny stillness, so that the youth could hear the pounding of his own heavy heart. He felt himself in the grip of an inescapable destiny; there were steps one had to take, regardless of personal profit or peril. There was something called duty.

On the bridge he found no sign of the captain.

"He has gone to his cabin, sir," said the navigating officer, pointing the way down a narrow passage.

Anton followed directions and knocked on a closed door. There was no answer, but he thought he could hear whispering and the sound of faint laughter inside. He hesitated, then knocked again. This time there were footsteps and the snapping of a bolt as the door opened.

The skipper's face appeared in the dimly lighted crack. It wore the expression—Anton knew without looking—of a man caught in his long underwear.

"Well, boy?" inquired the master of the *Teresa Taya,* his eyes blinking myopically. "What is it?"

Again the Archduke paused, but he manned himself and handed over the paper.

"Orders from Genoa to turn back the ship, sir."

The message disappeared through the crack and the door closed. What transpired in the captain's stateroom after that could have been told only by an eyewitness.

Sick at heart, Anton returned below deck. He felt like a traitor to his own blood. Haunted by visions of Ekaterinburg where the Czar and his hapless family had been slaughtered only a year ago, the tormented youth could not sleep that night.

Next morning he was the first on deck, studying the ship's log which was posted daily on the poop. Oddly, there were no indications of a change in course. Had the captain disregarded official orders?

Later during the day the Romanian dancer appeared for her morning stroll. She walked with swaying hips, talking loudly to a brace of officers at her side.

"Imagine," she said, "some silly message ordering the boat to turn back, and me with the best engagement of my career going *poof!* I would sue for one million *pesetas!* And the captain, him I would kill!"

With gaping mouth the Archduke Anton watched her pass. She caught the stupefied expression on his face and took it to be tribute to her irresistible allure. He looked a trifle young, a mere child, she thought. Still, she was woman enough to evaluate the special gifts of innocence. She rewarded Anton with her most radiant smile.

The boy flushed. Had his stare been equivocal, unseemly? Painted women had smiled at him before, during Vienna schooldays, but Pater Gregor's strict precepts had taught him to fear their wiles. Certainly the dancing girl was tawdry and obvious enough. But she embodied at this moment his own salvation and that of all he held dear. To Anton, therefore, she appeared lovely beyond words. He smiled back.

Later in the day the mystery of the disregarded Genoese orders acquired a less romantic complexion. Gossip between passengers and crew brought out that the captain had contraband aboard and could not risk turning back for another inspection. Regardless of the true explanation, the archducal family was safe and could now concentrate all energies on worrying about the step that lay immediately ahead. Would they be allowed to land in Spain? What fate awaited them there?

For the moment such worries were premature, as there was once more an abrupt change in weather. The squall returned, this time with inconceivable force. The fury of the storm threw the vessel about with such violence that the propeller spun wildly above the surface of the sea, sending a quiver to the very mast tops. A plate tore loose in the ship's side and the churning sea poured in. Safety doors were closed, cutting off the damaged section, but not before a flood of water had reached the engine room. To make matters worse, the pumps had been jammed by the terrible vibration. All hands—including passengers—were needed for bailing.

This was wonderful for the children, who threw themselves excitedly into action. Barefooted, they slushed about in the water and scooped up great buckets to carry above deck. They felt enormously important. A hand pump had meanwhile been discovered, which was promptly operated by Signor d'Aquila and a big-muscled stoker. Yes, even in the face of mortal danger, it was a magnificent and exhilarating experience.

Having been enlisted as workers, many of the passengers forgot even to be seasick, though haplessly not all. At one point, as the younger archdukes, Franz Josef and Carlos, leaned out of a double porthole there was a retching sound overhead. They wriggled back, but not in time. Indicative of the severity of the storm were the lifeboats, swinging low from their davits, ready for occupancy at the first alarm.

The prolonged inclemency of the weather naturally caused considerable delay. The short dash from Genoa to Barcelona, usually negotiated in thirty hours, took five days. The captain's girl friend was frantic by this time over her Madrid contract. Her cooing had turned to curses and recriminations.

At last, on the afternoon of the fifth day, the coast of Catalonia was in sight. It was now that a touching occurrence took place aboard ship.

Among the stewards there was a Spanish adherent of the famed Carlist party, which opposed the rule of Alfonso XIII. This ardent patriot had somehow got wind that a daughter of Don Carlos, the late Pretender, was aboard the *Teresa Taya*. He had spent the entire voyage searching for the highborn lady, so as to render homage at her feet. What feminine passengers appeared on deck did not fit his description of an Infanta of Castile. Furthermore, since Madame Navarre had voluntarily confined herself to her cabin, the steward's search was bound to remain fruitless.

Only now, at sight of her ancestral land, did the Spanish Princess cast off her disguise. As the Infanta Blanca, Archduchess of Austria, she at last stepped forth from her retreat.

It was the steward's great moment.

He recognized her instantly, even though he had never seen either her face or photograph before this moment. With an exclamation he fell to his knees, kissing the hem of her robe.

"Your Highness," he stammered, "I was a soldier under His Majesty, Don Carlos——"

She admonished him in kindly yet stern words. "My father was never king—you must not call him that. We come as beggars to ask shelter of Don Alfonso. I pray, do not embarrass me!"

The man withdrew, and the Infanta turned to the hardest task she had ever been called upon to perform. She addressed a message to the monarch, whose rule she and her nearest of kin would always challenge. It cost her a measure of pride to stand thus—a petitioner—before the enemy of her line, soliciting admittance for herself and her family to this same monarch's realm. Yet in her humiliation there was a mingling of composure and authority, for the Legitimists to whom she belonged had strong convictions. But for the rolling of political dice, her own brother, the present Pretender Don Jaime, would occupy the throne in Alfonso's place. . . .

Even while she wrote, a tender had arrived from the docks to bring the harbor patrol aboard. Passengers whose visas were in order made ready to debark. A short while later the small craft chugged back to shore, carrying its human cargo and the Infanta's message to the King. No travelers remained aboard the *Teresa Taya* save the archducal family.

From the ship's prow Anton and his younger brothers gazed across the bay toward the dock area of Barceloneta. While Franz Josef and Carlos speculated on whether the *Schinackerl* (Viennese idiom for tugs that plied the Danube Canal) would return to fetch them, Anton was secretly worried.

What had become of the wireless dispatch from Genoa? Once the captain got his contraband safely ashore, would he denounce the remaining passengers as fugitives sought by the Italian and Austrian police? True, Mama had penned a message to Alfonso. But they might all be arrested and put on another ship before the King in far Madrid looked over his morning mail.

Regretfully Anton discovered that a conscience is a heavy burden, at times to be dropped advisedly as ballast, just as he ought to have dropped that wireless dispatch into the sea.

Chapter Nine

THE REASON THAT the Infanta Blanca could not enter her ancestral country without official permission hinged upon the fact that she was a Carlist. Carlism hinges upon history.

Its explanation goes back to the peninsular campaigns of Napoleon the Great and the puppet rule of his brother Joseph Bonaparte at Madrid. In 1814, after the French star had begun to wane, Joseph was driven out and the Bourbon Ferdinand VII was restored to the Spanish throne.

Unusual among Most Catholic kings, Ferdinand could not be apostrophized The Fertile. He married three times without producing any heirs, male or female. Automatically this placed his brother Carlos in line for the succession.

But to everyone's surprise, Ferdinand essayed a fourth marriage, this time to Maria Cristina of Naples. One way or another this lady presented him with a brace of daughters, Isabella and Maria Luisa.

The belated arrival of these babies in no wise changed the status of Don Carlos. He was still heir to his brother's throne, since the Spanish monarchy operated under Salic Law, which does not permit women to inherit a crown.

The Neapolitan-born Queen, who had a Vesuvian temper, resented this decree. She belabored her docile spouse in an effort to have it revoked, so that one of her daughters might someday wield the scepter. Ferdinand demurred. He respected his ancestors and the royal code they had handed down to him. He knew the unconstitutionality of his wife's request. But he was also worn out by four turns at matrimony and his powers of resistance had declined.

To escape distasteful arguments, Ferdinand alleged some

obscure malady and took to his bed where, since the Queen followed him, he found no peace. The controversies continued until in the end his health really gave way, though not before Maria Cristina laid a cunning plan. On parchment she drew up a manifesto nullifying the *Lex Salica*. As the King lay dying, she forced a quill into his hand and guided it across the page. The hand grew cold and stiff, but she pushed on to the final signature. At Ferdinand's death on September 29, 1833, the young Isabella II ascended the throne, with her mother acting as regent until the child's majority.

Protests were launched by Don Carlos, Isabella's uncle, who naturally refused to recognize the deathbed legislation. All Spain was divided as people took issue, some maintaining that the dying King could do no wrong, while others sneered that he could have been wronged. The latter group allied itself with Don Carlos, upholding him as legal heir to the throne. They raised an army of determined partisans and plunged the country into the First Carlist War.

Maria Cristina for her part was not idle. She lined up the government forces against the rebels and offered a stiff resistance. Since she had a standing army at her command while Don Carlos must organize and equip fresh recruits, the struggle was uneven from the start. All the advantages lay with the party in the saddle, namely the little Queen and her maternal regent. For the avuncular Pretender it was added gall to realize that his opposition would be predominantly feminine, but he could not afford to let this fact deter him. He had too much at stake.

Though Isabella was the actual bone of contention, she had precious little to say in the matter. Even the campaign name by which the Queen's adherents became known identified them with her mother, for they called themselves *Los Cristinos*.

Interest in this royal scrimmage was not confined to Spain. Across the Pyrenees sat another Bourbon (of the Orléans line), King Louis Philippe of France. This worthy gentleman had learned something from Napoleon, namely that one could encourage incompetence among the neighbors and then profitably step in to offer them aid. If Madrid, for example, remained at cross purposes, the government of Spain might well be run from Paris. Another thing: if the Pretender Don Carlos dethroned the little Queen and set up his own line, the future succession was insured. For this farseeing claimant and his Portuguese wife, Francisca de Braganza, had a well-stocked nursery of young Carlistas to bolster the cause. But Isabella, herself still a child, might never have children. . . .

This gave Louis Philippe to think.

If Isabella *de facto* never did have children, her relatives, the French Bourbons, could put in a rival claim for the Spanish throne. According to such arithmetic Don Carlos was really the enemy of France! Imbued with love of country, Louis Philippe decided to throw his lot with Isabella against those would-be usurpers, *Los Carlistas*.

One angle still troubled him: how to keep Isabella from having children.

During the Middle Ages such minor considerations formed no stumbling block. Necromancy, plus the practical aid of specific herbs, could make women unfit for their normal destiny of motherhood. But modern ethics no longer viewed such reasonable measures in the light of mere utility; besides, there was no way to get at little Isabella. One must think of something better.

If he was nothing else, Louis Philippe was resourceful. In

no time at all he had the perfect solution. There circulated about the French court any number of nobles more or less related to the Bourbon-Orléans line. One of these, Prince François d'Assisi, had a colorful career of uncanonical sexual activity behind him, with the result that he was notoriously sterile. What could be more fitting than to marry him to the Spanish Queen?

A letter proposing this was penned to the Regent, Maria Cristina, without of course mentioning the prospective bridegroom's shortcomings. In return for their consent to the match, Louis Philippe pledged himself to aid the Cristinos in their fight against Don Carlos.

It was a brilliant move, touching the Queen Mother in her most vulnerable spot. Her hatred for her ambitious brother-in-law had become an all-consuming flame. Any means that might aid her in crushing him was acceptable, nay, welcome! She seized upon the French offer with unqualified enthusiasm. Let Isabella's suitor come—the sooner the better!

As an afterthought the impassioned lady recalled that her daughter was only thirteen years old, hardly a marriageable age. No matter: a special edict could be passed, declaring a state of emergency, which necessitated advancement of Isabella's majority by a few seasons.

While they were about it, the royal matchmakers took care of Isabella's sister too. For Maria Luisa the French monarch offered another seedy cousin, the Duc de Montpensier. Together with Isabella's marriage the betrothal of the younger girl was to be announced. This sewed up the Spanish problem neatly and to Louis Philippe's complete satisfaction.

Surprisingly, it was the young Isabella who in the end thwarted her Parisian uncle's plans. She married François, to be sure, and she was as miserable with him as everyone in France expected. But there were consequences nobody had foreseen. The young Queen was hot-blooded and hungry for love. After a few years of virginal wedlock she turned from her impotent consort and sought satisfaction elsewhere. A string of lovers moved through the palace at Madrid. Moreover, they were as Spanish as Gibraltar and the bull rings of Seville, for Isabella had nothing but contempt for effete courtiers and grandees who reminded her of poor François. Like Catherine the Great of Russia, she picked her paramours from the ranks of the army and the palace guard, with an occasional matador or stableboy thrown in for variety.

It becomes necessary to record that the Queen's bedfellows were not sterile. Fertility was rampant in the royal boudoir, as Isabella gave birth time and again to healthy infants of the most undeniably Spanish stock. At last here were heirs to the throne whose blood bore kinship to *El Cid!* Only, they were illegitimate.

Louis Philippe was very much put out. Sputtering with righteous indignation, he dispatched countless letters to Isabella, rapping her immorality. Though French, he talked to her like a Dutch uncle, pointing out that the world was scandalized by her behavior. But Isabella had no time for correspondence. The wrathful epistles piled up on her desk unread.

The exasperated Louis Philippe now addressed himself to François, ordering that sorry figure to brand the Queen's profuse offspring as bastards. Failing this, France would have no excuse to make Spain its political ward.

But François had suffered a change of heart. Far from disclaiming parenthood, he was sunning himself in borrowed glory. In his younger years he had been a flagrant roué of international reputation; in fact, he had enjoyed his reputation almost more than the pleasures that gave rise to it. But in time his failing prowess had become the gossip of Parisian drawing rooms, and François was plunged into the depths of melancholia. Not enough that he must bear his degradation—people *knew* about it!

And then kind Fate offered a poultice for his injured vanity. Even at the cost of multiple horns (more, indeed, than he could accommodate on his slight cranium) François saw a chance for vicarious vindication. After he and Isabella had been wed, the royal nursery at Madrid was rapidly being peopled with a swarm of infants, all of whom he could claim publicly as his own. Yes, he would claim that he had sired each and every one; no King of France could make him out a cuckold!

With this development the Cristinos had won a double victory. Not only had Louis Philippe helped them conclude the First Carlist War with rampant success, but the line of Isabella II was now more firmly entrenched than ever.

Triumph went to the young Queen's head. Up to now she had been pampered by an adoring and ambitious mother, while the amorous routine of her life had schooled her in boundless self-indulgence. She became inordinately spendthrift, a foible always reflected in increased national taxation. Grumbling began to be heard throughout the land, always ending in the same refrain: "The upkeep of a royal family costs too much—republics are cheaper!"

The Queen paid no attention until, one day, her exchequer pointed out that the taxpayers had gone on strike. There were no funds coming in.

At this, Isabella's temper rose. Like a spoiled child, she screamed and spat in the faces of those about her. She shouted orders that every defaulting citizen was to be rounded up and thrown into jail. Already a harlot and a fool, she now became a despot.

For the last of these no Spaniard would stand.

In 1868 the Revolution broke out. An anti-royalist mob surrounded the palace in Madrid, demanding the Queen's abdication. But Isabella had dodged this unpleasant eventuality by escaping with her brood the night before. By the time her absence was discovered, the royal cavalcade had already reached the border at Pamplona and crossed into France.

Having cleaned house, the Spanish patriots set up a provisional republic. But they were inexperienced in the mechanics of democratic government, which afforded adventurers and opportunists a chance for easy graft. Before long the experiment threatened to become more costly than ever the monarchy had been, without the satisfaction of having a culprit on whom to pin responsibility. In a monarchy there was always the head of state whose neck could be publicly wrung; but a democracy had many heads, each hiding behind another, with actual guilt resting on none. To the average Spaniard this seemed too muddled for practical use. After two years under a republic, the Spanish people voted for another king. But they were tired of French interference, hence they did not want another Bourbon.

Of course, no sooner did the news spread abroad that the vacant throne of Madrid might welcome an occupant, than a great hullabaloo was set up among the vastly expanding circles of "pretenders." No longer was Don Carlos the only figure strutting about under that purposeful caption. The dethroned Isabella and her children were in the market too. In addition, there was Isabella's sister, Maria Luisa, whose marriage to the Duc de Montpensier had turned out to be surprisingly fruitful—contributing to the total of eager claimants. And lastly, the lovers of the Queen put in their bid, basing their somewhat impudent demands on service rendered at stud.

Firmly rejecting all such entanglements, the Spanish Cortes in full parliamentary session stood their ground and decided to search abroad for a candidate of different caliber.

In England an ever-alert Queen Victoria scanned the photographs of her plentiful Saxe-Coburg-Gotha nephews, in anticipation of a visit from the Spanish Ambassador. But Her Majesty's assiduity was premature; no Protestant was wanted at Madrid.

King Ferdinand of Portugal felt himself qualified to hold down a double job, should Spain care to throw in its lot with the Braganzas of Lisbon. But Spain thought not. To run a single country, however small, was a full-time task. Such, at least, was the opinion of the Cortes.

There remained the House of Savoy with, haplessly, no prince available at this time; and there was the Catholic branch of Hohenzollern-Sigmaringen. The latter boasted a handsome blond scion by the name of Leopold. Overjoyed at their discovery of him, the royal commission did not bother to find out whether Leopold was as bright as he was fair. They simply made him an offer.

Before he could polish up his speech of acceptance there was a storm of protest out of France, where Napoleon III had meanwhile become emperor after first serving as president of the second French republic that followed the death, in 1850, of Louis Philippe.

The Bonaparte of the mustaches and goatee had no Bourbon sympathies, but he emphatically did not want a German prince perched on the throne of Spain. His emissary said as much to the Foreign Minister of the Reich, Prince Otto von Bismarck-Schönhausen. The objection was couched in

Franz Josef on delivery boy's tricycle in courtyard of the
Palais Toscana, Vienna.

Standing: Anton, Leopold, Rainer; *sitting:* Franz Josef; *baby:* Carlos.

the language of an ultimatum: Leopold must refuse the Spanish offer, or France would mobilize.

A gleam came into Bismarck's eye. He had waited long for a chance to measure Prussia's strength against the French. The obscure Leopold and his prospect of ruling a second-rate power like Spain meant nothing to the future Iron Chancellor. But as a pretext for war anything would do. The gauntlet was hurled back.

The fracas that followed is variously recorded by historians as the Franco-Prussian War, the War of 1870, or the War of the Spanish Succession. Actually the last of these, though least in use, is the most accurate designation. The empty throne at Madrid had furnished the motive. But once hostilities had broken out, Spain was forgotten; she had not even been invited, by either side, to put an army in the field.

Crestfallen, the Cortes reassembled in Madrid and announced that the candidacy of Leopold von Hohenzollern-Sigmaringen looked hopeless. The search for another royal replacement was on.

At this point Italy found that she had an unemployed princelet after all. He was Duke Amadeo of Aosta, second son of Victor Emmanuel II. This agreeable young man accepted an offer from the Spanish Cortes on November 16, 1870, and arrived at Madrid's palace of El Pardo the following January. Under a ministry led by Serrano, Sagasta, and Ruiz Zorrilla, he donned the crown that had gone so long begging.

He became the only King Amadeo in Spanish history.

Fortune did not smile upon his reign, for there were still the die-hard Carlists waiting to make a comeback. Their chance appeared during the increasing turmoil of the Franco-Prussian War. While Bismarck and Napoleon were figuratively at each other's throats the perennial Pretender issued a new call to battle. Needless to say, the Second Carlist War ended as hopelessly as the previous failure.

Meanwhile there remained democratic elements in Spain which did not favor shelving the Republic. With considerable pluck this group banded together and fought against both Amadeo and his enemies, the Carlists. By terrorist acts, such as an attempt on Amadeo's life, followed by threats against the Pretender, royalty's cause was again driven under cover. Before long Amadeo regretted his regal aspirations. Tired of the whole thing, he packed his bags and returned posthaste to his home in Turin.

With Don Carlos beaten and Amadeo gone, the Cortes now pronounced that the Republic would have to continue willy-nilly. There was no taker for the crown. None, that is, save the unwanted Bourbons.

While arms clashed around Metz and Sedan, bringing Napoleon's Empire down over his ears, Spain muddled along under three presidents who followed each other within the space of a single year. Their names alone are remembered, since they had no time for deeds. Successively they were: Pi y Margall, Salmerón, and Castelar.

All this while, undercover intrigue went on among exiled dynasts for a return to the fleshpots of Madrid. The Cristinos, the Carlistas, the Montpensiers, and Isabella's lovers felt themselves more than ever in the running. And, in the end, the Cortes weakened and invited Isabella's eldest son (by what father, no one knew) to ascend the throne as Alfonso XII. Again the Bourbons were in power.

To keep this power a family matter, Alfonso was persuaded by his mother and aunt to marry his cousin Mercedes, third daughter of Maria Luisa and the Duc de Montpensier. The couple were united in 1874, but the bride scarcely survived the honeymoon, dying within five months.

Another marriage was arranged, this time with the bluest blood in Europe, the House of Habsburg. Archduchess Maria Cristina was the new bride. Her name had been considered a good omen, since it duplicated that of Alfonso's energetic grandmother.

The wedding took place in 1879. But now it was the bridegroom who had been marked for death. After the birth of two daughters—the Princess of the Asturias, in 1880, and the Infanta Maria Teresa, two years later—the King expired on November 25, 1885, leaving no male issue.

This circumstance revitalized the languished Carlist cause, since the ghost of the Salic Law had never been quite laid. There were always those who argued eloquently against women wearing trousers or crowns—in monarchic parlance the same thing. In short, the Legitimist movement had received a tingling shot in the arm.

Actually the Pretender was no longer the original Don Carlos, but his grandson, bearing the same name and the burden of the family feud. For three generations the grievance had been handed down without diminishing in bitterness; the present Carlos wore a pout as indefatigably as his father and grandfather before him. To be a pretender was by now a profession.

He had no trouble recruiting an army of followers. Issuing a manifesto to the nation, the claimant of the moment marched on Madrid, and the Third Carlist War was on.

Again only defeat lay in store. The cards were stacked against this Carlos as surely as they had been against his forebears. For the widowed Queen had an ace up her sleeve, or rather, a manchild in her womb: the future Alfonso XIII, born posthumously on May 17, 1886. The Austrian lady's reticence regarding her interesting condition had caused this most unseasonable revival of Carlist hopes, which ended by being ignominiously dashed.

Hereafter the Legitimist movement faded almost completely. With his mother serving as regent during his minority, Alfonso XIII ascended the throne in 1902 and three years later married Princess Ena of Battenberg, granddaughter of Queen Victoria, who had once proposed a Coburg nephew for Madrid. Something might have been made of the fact that Ena was a Protestant, but before enemy factions could exploit this failing it became known that she had been converted to the Catholic faith before entering Spain. In token of this the Pope had bestowed upon her a singular distinction, the Order of the Golden Rose.

For Don Carlos there was not much more to do. Exiled from Spain, he retired to Palazzo Loredan on the Grand Canal in Venice, one of the properties acquired by his predecessors during similar enforced sojourns abroad. Here he enjoyed one more bittersweet flash of adulation which, however, was not directed at his person. An unknown man begged for an interview one day and, being admitted, walked through the richly carpeted salon into the presence of Don Carlos. The latter was at his pictorial best, with Basque beret on his head and a handsome Great Dane at his side, for he was about to take a stroll.

The stranger dropped on both knees, his flushed face almost touching the floor.

"Ah, Your Royal Highness——" he gasped, overcome with emotion.

Don Carlos likewise was moved, to the point indeed of giving up his walk. In his most gracious though seignorial manner he bade the stranger rise.

"Now, now, my good man," said the Prince of Spain, "what brings you here?"

At this the stranger manned himself. "Never in all my years as a rug merchant," he exclaimed, "have I seen such beautiful Bokharas!"

It developed thereupon that the extraordinary caller had heard about the lavish furbishings of Loredan and, finding the master in, had nerved himself to call.

For Don Carlos this was perhaps the ultimate disillusion, if not the deathblow to ambition. At any rate, he received no more callers.

Withdrawing from public life, he died on July 18, 1909. The mantle of presumptive royalty fell upon his son, Don Jaime, who thenceforth must take up the cudgels and maintain the family claim.

It was Don Jaime's sister, the Infanta Blanca, who waited now on a bleak January day in 1919 outside Barcelona harbor for permission from His Majesty, Alfonso XIII, to enter Spain.

Chapter Ten

FOREIGN MINISTER COUNT ÁLVARO DE FIGUEROA ROMANONES paced the audience chamber in the royal palace at Madrid.

"Your Majesty," he addressed his master, Alfonso XIII, "this is a question involving the safety of the realm."

The King's lips parted and Romanones observed what others had before: when Alfonso smiled one forgot that he was ugly.

"The Infanta Blanca dangerous? Nonsense!"

"Extremely so," insisted the statesman. "Carlista sentiment is not dead in Spain. With the arrival of Don Jaime's sister false hopes may be fanned in undesirable quarters. I beg Your Majesty to take precautions——"

"Precautions? What would you have me do?"

"Refuse the request for admission, Sire."

"But I am cousin to her. She is homeless, begging shelter for herself and family——"

Romanones became icy. "As Your Majesty's Minister, I am compelled to counsel objective and impersonal thinking. That is, where enemies of Spain are concerned."

"You persist in calling the Infanta an enemy?"

"I do. Don Jaime is exiled to Paris; let his sister join him there."

The King frowned helplessly. "But she has an Austrian husband and Austrian children who would instantly be taken prisoners and shipped off to some forsaken island, as is usually the fate of royal refugees——"

"Fortunes of war . . ." shrugged Romanones.

Alfonso rose. "Well, I am a neutral. I do not accept fortunes of war befalling those who by an accident of birth are mere pawns in the game. The Infanta is to enter Spain!"

Romanones paled. In private life he was a millionaire exporter of oils, hence he had a personal stake in forestalling
political risks. His almost fanatical watchfulness over the
nation's social and economic equilibrium was sincere; up-
heavals—particularly revolutions—were bad for business.

"If that is Your Majesty's decision," he put in with well-
calculated emphasis, "I urge that Doña Blanca and her family be confined in a safe place, say the fortress of Gerona,
under military guard."

Alfonso shook his head. "No, Romanones, that would be
an indignity!"

"Is treason better, Sire?"

The King flushed. "There will be no treason. I shall put
the Infanta on her honor. She shall have the freedom of my
realm on condition that she will engage in no Carlist intrigue."

"And what will be our guarantee, Your Majesty?"

"*That,* Romanones, you may not understand—the word of
an Infanta of Castile!"

The King gave a little nod, indicating that the meeting
was concluded. He walked quickly from the room. In an
antechamber he paused and gave orders to a secretary:

"Telephone the Barcelona port authorities that the remaining passengers on the *Teresa Taya* are to be brought ashore.
A personal wire from me will follow."

The secretary bowed and picked up a receiver.

Half an hour later the waters of Barcelona Bay were
churned into a froth as the tender chugged importantly out
toward the anchored ship.

"Here comes the *Schinackerl!*" cried the children from
their lookout, where they had stood watch for hours. "We
are going to land!"

Their parents felt less certain. They waited quietly, trying to conceal whatever misgivings assailed them. In another moment the suspense would be over and they would know what was in store.

With Alfonso's message finally in her hands, the Infanta Blanca wept. She turned to her husband:

"Our wanderings are over!"

At this instant the Carlist steward, who had slipped back with the tender, stepped up to whisper that a deputation of Legitimist patriots awaited Her Royal Highness at the docks. The Infanta glared at him fiercely.

"Then I order you back ashore at once," she said sharply, "before any of us step off this boat! Tell them to disband. I come to Spain as a private citizen, without political designs."

It was not easy for her to scorn demonstrations of loyalty to a cause with which her line had been identified for almost a century. But she did not, on the other hand, feel called upon to pick up the all but extinguished Carlist torch. With monarchies tottering everywhere it would be insanity to fan anti-royal sentiments by boring from within. As Alfonso's guest it was her duty to support Alfonso.

The steward skulked away unhappily, more certain than ever of the intrinsic rightness of Salic Law. Women could not be entrusted with sacred national issues. They had no sense of destiny. Would that, in place of the Infanta, Don Jaime had reappeared! The tocsin of revolt and of Legitimist rebirth would certainly have sounded throughout Spain.

Far from such thoughts, Doña Blanca was busy with landing preparations. The luggage had been piled on deck, ready to be lowered by means of a hoist. A minor tragedy now occurred as the net, employed normally for the unloading of bulkier freight, proved too wide of mesh for the

Archduke Franz Ferdinand and his family.

1882. Carlos.

Don Carlos of Spain and his son, Don Jaime.

skimpy archducal pieces. A number of bags toppled helter-skelter into the sea. Loud cries of distress accompanied the ensuing splash:

"There goes Mama's *sacoche* (suitcase)!"

"And Anton's camera——"

"And the coffer with the Golden Fleece!"

This last was a real loss, for the *Kollane* or Grand Collar that went with the award of knighthood in the ancient order remained in the bearer's hands only on loan. Emblems of the Fleece, in miniature or full size, could be purchased in quantity, but the gem-encrusted chain reverted to the Vienna *Ballae* (Keepers of the Vault). The Order had originally embraced only twenty-four members, all of whom must be crowned heads of kingdoms or empires; this requisite had since been abandoned and the Knights now numbered eighty. Of these the Archduke Leopold Salvator had been the last, hence the Riband remained in his possesion in token of recent investiture.

Mama's *sacoche,* though without historical value, proved almost an equally poignant loss, for it contained the family album, falsified passports, some silver tableware and three priceless bars of soap.

In the end, however, it was decided that they had all been lucky, losing only a few pieces of baggage rather than their lives. After all, one of the children might have dropped overboard and vanished into the waters of Barcelona Bay.

After the baggage episode the debarkation proceeded without incident. In the pale glow of a winter sunset the Infanta set foot on the land of her ancestors while, trailing diffidently behind, her Austrian husband and offspring studied the unfamiliar scene.

There was no time for sightseeing that same day, as sleeping quarters must be found before dark. Alfonso's hospitality had after all not included a castle put at the refugees' disposal; such courtesies were prescribed by protocol only in the case of visiting rulers who were at the peak of their power. When royalty was in trouble, palaces grew scarce.

In short, it was up to the Austrians to fend for themselves and find a place to stay.

While they roamed about Barcelona streets the city's strange architectural face startled the Vienna visitors. The touch of Antonio Gaudi y Cornet, an artist with extraordinary and original views on housing, was everywhere to be seen. Fantastic curves and angles, combining cubism and Churrigueresque Baroque in shocking convolutions, fronted the great avenue of Las Cortes Catalanas.

Looking for lodgings in this maze of modernism was disconcerting when cheapness of price was a prime consideration. With their scant wardrobe and even skimpier funds the Habsburg guests had no wide range of choice. Thus the list of fashionable hotels was quickly disregarded in favor of a second-rate hostelry called the Bristol. It was short on bathrooms, bedsprings, and beauty—but suitable in price. As in Trieste and Genoa, the family doubled up in order to save space: Mama and the girls slept in one large room, while the masculine contingent took a smaller one next door.

Before retiring, a conference was held in order to take stock of available resources. First of all the trunks and boxes must be opened for a general clothes inspection. Franz Josef was still wearing the shirt he had brought from school, hence it was necessary to take one from Anton and cut it down to size. But other tailoring needs became now apparent. One of the girls, the Archduchess Immaculata, had lost all her dresses in the very first suitcase that had dropped overboard. A smaller handbag bearing her name stood safely in the room, but it contained only Mozart sonatas and a Haydn score for violin. Immaculata was something of a prodigy, particularly on the piano. But if you have nothing to wear, there is little comfort in *"Eine Kleine Nachtmusik."*

The first week in Barcelona went by with fittings and feverish sewing bees under Mama's observing eye, while next door Papa and his sons acquainted themselves with the art of ironing a pair of presentable pants.

It became, in a way, an exhilarating experience. There was satisfaction in finding out how much one could really do without help from others. The servant staff of Galitzin Hill would certainly have been impressed.

Nevertheless, Papa was low in spirits. He had not been able to put out of his mind the loss of the Riband of the Golden Fleece.

"It was not ours to lose!" he repeated over and over. "We were responsible. I must find a way for its replacement."

This would be a major undertaking for a cashiered military chief. The Archduke Leopold Salvator was no financial wizard. Expropriated and ruined, he could hardly hope to recoup his fortunes in civilian life, much less spare the cost of an incalculable historic treasure.

While he worried about the Golden Fleece the Infanta wondered where the next meal was coming from. Still, she was not without sympathy for her husband's pother.

"Why don't you write Stepanek," she proposed, "and tell him to sell the Hortense Diadem? It should bring enough to make good on the lost *Kollane*."

The older children urged the same step, made necessary by their father's uncompromising honesty. If he failed to cover the debt, Papa would not sleep.

As for the Hortense Diadem, though the Infanta had always worn it as her own, it was a Habsburg heirloom belonging to Papa, for him to do with as he chose. In an un-hinged world where another investiture of the Golden Fleece was not likely to occur for the next hundred years, the Archduke Leopold Salvator worried nevertheless about restoring a jeweled chain. Yes, they were very proud of Papa. A letter must be written to Stepanek, instructing him to ne-gotiate the sale of the diadem. At Barcelona, meanwhile, Mama could dispose of another emerald and pay the rent.

It was surprising what a single gem, and on this occasion not a particularly large one, could do. The family lived at the Bristol for six months and later moved to a house on the Avenida Tibidabo near the edge of town. Here the young archduchesses learned to sweep and cook, while the smaller boys alternated with their father in marketing and perform-ing outdoor chores. The whole family took up gardening. Papa studied seed catalogues and presently he was all set for growing the needs of the daily table.

"One must start with a compost heap in the back yard," he declared after bargaining with a neighborhood dealer for a cartload of manure. "Every farmer has a compost heap."

Next he laid out the narrow stretch of garden into plots, one for each of the children and himself (the Infanta with-drew from this picturesque enterprise). With the arrival of spring a lively competition ensued as salad greens, carrots, beans, and potatoes sprouted in prodigal abundance. By summer an added bonanza developed as an apple tree from the orchard next door leaned heavily across the garden wall and promised a harvest of autumnal droppings.

"We can make cider from that," said Papa, paging the booklet on home-brewery and distillation. He was prepared for every contingency.

By noon, when household and gardening chores were done, Mama took over. After lunch she resumed the reading sessions that had formed so rigorous a part of the children's Vienna schedule. But she no longer focused on the French Revolution or the terrors of the Commune. They knew these things today from actual experience. What they all needed now was to perfect their Spanish, so that the younger children in particular could enter local schools.

The Infanta's teaching methods were simplicity itself. She made everybody read aloud in turn. While this went on she peered over the reader's shoulder, pointing with a pencil from one word to the next. Whenever she caught a wrongly accented syllable or a mistake in pronunciation the pencil stopped moving. There was silence while the pupil wondered what to do. Yet only in extreme cases did Mama prompt.

"Try again," was her principle. "If it won't work one way, it must another. You learn best that which you teach yourself."

All the while she too was learning. She had adjusted herself to the change from a castle with eighty-six liveried servants to a house with no servants at all. At her age (she was now past fifty) the contrast proved a greater strain than she herself had suspected. On Galitzin Hill a staff of housekeepers and major-domos had directed domestic operations, while today the Infanta found it exhausting to steer five inexperienced daughters through the duties involved in ordinary living. Since she drove herself with equally relentless discipline the good lady was soon prostrated with fatigue.

There was a family conclave headed by Papa. Something must be done to ease Mama's burden. The proceeds from the second emerald, which had seen them through the Bristol sojourn and paid for the move to Avenida Tibidabo, had not yet vanished. But the Infanta hoarded every *céntimo* that was left. This, despite the fact that living expenses had been cut down by the acquisition of some chickens, to provide eggs and an occasional fricassee for the archducal table.

Well, a way must be found to make Mama loosen her purse strings. Also, and this was more important, an inexpensive maid must be hired to help the Infanta grapple with the chores she had set herself.

"I've seen an employment agency downtown," said the Archduchess Dolores, who went on long walks to overcome a limp (she had been crippled by a childhood injury).

Carlos added a bit of information. "That's where the apothecary's wife on the corner got an orphan. Orphans are cheap!"

It was worth considering. By bedtime the decision had been reached that Dolores and her sisters would stop the following day at the employment agency. They might nerve themselves to ask for an orphan, like the one that worked for the apothecary's wife.

It was thus that a girl named Soledad Golo y Mendáriz entered the service of the Infanta Blanca of Spain.

Chapter Eleven

On leaving the Convent of Santa Brígida, Soledad had known that the career of a domestic lay before her.

She who dreamed of great learning, of passing the provincial examinations with honor, and perhaps even aspiring to one of Spain's leading universities—Salamanca, Saragossa, Valladolid—had been dismissed before finishing intermediate school, because one charity case must make room for another.

Gone was the hope of returning to her native village as a *profesora* who would lift the peasants from their ignorance. Her vision of a small, whitewashed schoolhouse where even gypsy children would be admitted, scrubbed, clothed and made fit for human contact, had faded abruptly into something quite different. There would be scrubbing, yes, but not for the uplift of the underprivileged. Instead it was to be menial work in the home of some rich *señora doña* who was too lazy to lace her own boots. At the agency, where Soledad and her companions had been sent straight from the orphanage, this was made quite clear.

"You are inexperienced," said the matron in charge. "I can place you only as *fregadoras* (scullery assistants)."

Twice before being offered for hire Soledad had tried to run away. But she was a ward of the Provincial Government and, while still a minor, subject to its authority. Escape was punished by confinement in some correctional institution. The matron issued this warning each night as she locked the girls' dormitory; they were technically free, but without choice in the disposition of that freedom. In return, the State was looking out for them. What more could they possibly ask?

Already half a dozen wards from Santa Brígida had been placed as dishwashers, nursemaids, or general scrubs in well-staffed households of Barcelona's merchant class. They accepted their lot without grumbling. Indeed, some had found quick advancement to better things. Red-haired Carola, for example, worked in the home of a prominent banker whose wife departed every summer for Biarritz. While alone, the banker liked hot chocolate served in bed, a chore to which Carola got herself promoted. It noticeably bolstered her salary.

Soledad did not expect as much. She could hardly see herself carrying breakfast to master bedrooms, no matter how good the tip.

On the other hand, when she was told that employment had been found for her in the home of an Infanta, whose husband was a foreigner of high title, Soledad did not rejoice. She was a stubborn Basque of republican convictions. Growing up in a village of rebels against monarchism, she had learned to hate class distinctions. Herein lay the root of her anger at being driven into servitude. Even so, she discriminated between possible employers. To work for the rich, or newly rich, at least meant working for those who themselves must once have worked and—inherited wealth being dissipated rapidly by incompetent heirs—would one day work again. It was the aristocrats whom Soledad could not tolerate: the idle, decorative parasites, born to title and privilege for which they lacked all justification. Because in medieval times a man fought bravely at Granada against the Moors must his descendants, fifteen generations hence, be hailed as grandees of Spain? What had unborn posterity to do with the exploits of great-grandsires whose heroism in any case was duplicated by common soldiers every day? Were not medals issued for gallantry? Today's conscripts in the war just ended must content themselves with less than that. For a leg shot off in battle they received a citation from their commanding officer plus a kiss on both cheeks. There were no patents of nobility to dazzle future generations for centuries to come.

It was with such sentiments as these that Soledad entered the house on Tibidabo Street.

She was due for a surprise, as the archducal family did not fit any of her preconceived notions. For one thing Soledad was startled to find no other servants.

"Is there no chambermaid?" she asked in honest amazement. "Who sweeps? Who cooks?"

The young archduchesses pointed to one another. "We take turns. You won't have much to do, really——"

The girl still did not grasp the situation. "But I am only a *fregadora,* to wash dishes——"

Dolores undertook to explain. "We won't need you for that. It's Mama you must look after. She is not so strong as she thinks, and she has never been without a—er—personal maid." (The term "lady-in-waiting" stuck in the Archduchess' throat. It did not sound well when spoken by refugees down on their luck.)

After these preliminaries Soledad was brought face to face with her new mistress. The Infanta put a hand on her shoulder.

"Your name, child?" she asked kindly.

"María de la Soledad Gola y Mendáriz."

The Infanta paused to consider. "A name of these parts," she mused. "Catalan or Basque?"

Soledad was slow to answer. She felt suspicious of this great lady with her simple manner.

"Basque, Your Highness———"

"I know your province well. I visited there as a child and even spoke your language, *Euskara.*" The Infanta could not resist indulging her erudition. "In olden times your country was called *Baskania,* which means Evil Eye———" She smiled. "I trust you are not so endowed?"

At the moment one might easily have thought this attribute present in Soledad's dark glance. For she had a serious face, with unexplored depths behind it. But the stubborn antagonism that had filled her when she first crossed the threshold of this house was rapidly going out of her. She felt limp and completely at sea.

"Soledad is a beautiful name, but a sad one," the Infanta continued. "It means Loneliness———"

"I am an orphan, Your Highness."

"Had they no nickname for you at the—er—school? A little pet name, something sweet?"

"They called me Chole."

"Chole———no, I don't like that. I think I shall call you Sol, after the sun that glazes the beaches of your country. Besides, Doña Sol is the name of a famous woman in one of Victor Hugo's plays, *Ruy Blas. . . .*"

Now, despite herself, Soledad was entranced. Never had anyone spoken to her in such terms before. She who had grieved at being denied an education was standing before a great lady who deemed her fit to enter a discussion about French literature. Of course Soledad did not believe in great ladies. She hated them.

"Well, Doña Sol?" said the Infanta. "What do you think?"

"I think—I think that I ought to go back to the agency."

It was the Infanta's turn to be nonplussed. "But why, my child—is the pay not adequate?" There had been as yet no talk of pay, but the archducal budget clearly could not be stretched very far. Board and a bit of pin money was all the Infanta dared offer. "We are poor," she said simply, "because we have no future . . ."

At this the girl blushed. "It is not a question of money——"

"No? Then what is it?"

"I am not, as Your Highness said, a child. In my village we know misery when we are very young. We hate all who have caused it—the powerful ones in high places, here and at Madrid. We are anti-royalist, Señora!"

There, she had said it. She had spat it out before the great lady with her magic powers could weave a spell about her. She had turned upon the noblewoman who was cousin to the King, refusing to be her servant.

"*Baskania,*" murmured the Infanta softly. "Perhaps I was mistaken, and you do have the Evil Eye——" Her voice was sad. "We have had much bad luck lately. I trust your hatred will not add to it."

Without answer the girl walked to the door. Watching her go, the older woman spoke again.

"I once had ladies-in-waiting. That is finished now. If you do not wish to serve me, will you stay and teach my daughters what—to my own dishonor—I cannot teach them myself?"

Soledad did not know why she halted on the threshold. It was assuredly against her will that she made answer to the Infanta's request. She could never forget the misery of her village, nor that it was the fault of the King and the King's kind. Yet she made answer:

"I will stay, Señora."

The Infanta nodded. "Thank you, Doña Sol——"

Life took on a new tempo after this. With a competent

young helper about the house, form took the place of confusion and schedules brought order into chaos. No longer did the rice burn on the kitchen stove while the particular archduchess who functioned as cook galloped upstairs to help the sister who darned hosiery or the one who made the beds. At the orphanage Soledad had learned organization. She brought it to the house on Tibidabo Street.

Actually, except for Assunta, Soledad was younger than the archducal daughters. Yet experience made her at times feel older even than their own mother. For there were moments when the Infanta Blanca herself seemed a mere child.

"Please have patience with Mama," confided Margareta one day. "She can't always hook herself up——"

It was unbelievable: the erstwhile Princess of Castile had never learned to dress or undress herself! She tried to conceal this from the accusing eyes of Soledad. Awkwardly she wriggled and twisted in her corsets to reach the snaps and buttons at the back of her frock, or stooped with creaking stays to lace up her always dainty kid boots. There were puffs and gasps through all this, as the Infanta had grown stout in middle age, and a trifle stiff in the joints for such unaccustomed gymnastics. On board ship, during the flight from Genoa, she had enlisted the help of her children— even small Carlos—to get properly rigged up. But now (she barely breathed this to herself) there was a Bolshevik in the house from whom one must learn the ways of a new social era. The Castilian lady vowed to negotiate her buttonholes or bust.

If the advent of Soledad proved salutary to the Infanta, it was a veritable boon to Papa. As head of the family the Archduke Leopold Salvator had taken upon himself the task of organizing its untrained members into a working community. This meant that he himself must proceed experimentally along paths heretofore unknown: the former Artillery Commander must wrestle now with such domestic problems as marketing, vegetable gardening, the balancing of a most precarious budget, and the performance of odd carpentry jobs about the house.

Soledad changed all this. With capable hand she took over the reins, releasing the master of the house for the more urgent duty of making a living. Leopold Salvator was everlastingly grateful to her. Not only did he welcome release from menial chores that put a strain on his dignity, but there had been brewing in his mind a scheme that might replenish family finances without robbing his good Blanca of another emerald.

Years ago, while Austria's prewar army idled comfortably through summer maneuvers, Leopold Salvator had enjoyed long stretches of leisure during which he could indulge personal hobbies, such as the assembling of a not inconsiderable stamp collection. He had exchanged philatelic information with a young captain on his staff, named Engelbert Dollfuss. Thanks to the latter's help, many a gem was added to the archducal albums, while in turn Dollfuss profited by his superior's largesse. By 1914 Salvator had tied up a neat fortune in stamps. Turned into cash, the collection could keep the archducal family in shoes and groceries for a normal span of life.

The difficulty was turning it into cash. In peaceful times there were always interested parties, including the King of England and an American millionaire or two. But the aftermath of war, with its threat of financial chaos darkening the horizon, dimmed all hope for capitalizing on expensive hobbies. Even the rare "blue Soudan" and the "Bengal Jubilee" went begging in the philatelist market, not to mention the triangular "Mauritius" or the "British Guiana of 1856."

In addition to this total lack of demand, the Archduke Leopold Salvator was not even certain of the whereabouts of his treasure. The hasty departure from Vienna had entailed so many worries concerning passports, tickets, transportation, food and clothes, that the comparatively trivial matter of safeguarding a stamp collection had been completely forgotten. By now the prized albums might well have gone the way of the hunting trophies and the castle plate. In short, Leopold Salvator was done with it. His mind had turned to something else.

From earliest youth the mysteries of mechanical engineering had fascinated him. In his military career it had been the machinery of battle that interested him far more than routines of strategy, tactics, parade etiquette, and drill. He was indifferent to statesmanship, for he held no international grudges and had no political ax to grind. At heart he had never really wanted to be a soldier; he fancied himself as an engineer.

Automobiles were Leopold Salvator's passion (inherited by all five of his sons). Even in the face of the old Emperor's prejudice against motorized vehicles, during the days before Karl and Zita, he had steadfastly improved Austria's archaic armies by adopting mechanical equipment. Old Franz Joseph's picturesque but impractical white cavalry had slowly but surely given way to Leopold Salvator's newfangled machines. The automobile, forbidden in the imperial mews of Schönbrunn, made its appearance in the artillery as early as 1908, somewhat easing the lot of Franz Joseph's successor, the Emperor Karl. If Karl made no showing in the war it was at least no fault of his legions; the army had come a long way since the equestrian pageantry that cost Franz Joseph the battle of Solferino. Austria's mechanized troops of 1914 were brave and well equipped. The fact that Karl could not finish the job, started by others long before he ascended the throne on November 21, 1916, was due in part to the Entente's formidable superiority, as well as to the young Emperor's disenchantment. The simple truth was that Karl had no heart for this war which had fallen as a grim inheritance upon his shoulders.

It might be construed as lack of patriotism that Leopold Salvator's penchant for tinkering with machinery did not diminish as the first hint of defeat clouded Austrian horizons. Even while battle reverses mounted and pessimism assailed the General Staff, the Chief of the Artillery employed leisure moments with a variety of mechanical experiments. He was an inventor. At long range this simple fact might conceivably be of greater import than the winning or losing of a war. Victory or defeat were relative concepts, purely temporary in significance. But a usable creation of the human brain was an advancement in which all mankind had a part.

Leopold Salvator was responsible for three inventions, two of which would be taken up and perfected by enthusiastic technicians of the future. The first of these was the development of four-wheel transmission, soon to be applied to military vehicles (including German Panzer cars no less than U.S. jeeps and trucks of World War II) in every corner of the globe. The premise on which this idea was based had long occupied the machine-minded Archduke. He had been irked by the fact that the front wheels of any motor car contributed nothing beyond balance and steering to its operation. Was this not a waste of potential driving power? Resolutely he set to work on a skeleton model, placing the differential in the center under the chassis and leading separate gears to each axle. In this way the loss of power was remedied as each wheel was forced to do its share.

The patent had first been offered to a Vienna industrialist named Wachalowski, though without shining results. Herr Wachalowski understandably concurred in the prevailing opinion that royal personages were decorative adjuncts to the national scene, but hardly to be taken seriously. Archdukes were known to break speed laws and otherwise make head-lines with their Daimlers or Hispano-Suizas, but was any-thing constructive to be expected from these hare-brained if ingratiating aristocrats? In short, Leopold Salvator's project was superficially scanned and returned with polite thanks.

The matter did not end there. An agent was employed to peddle the invention abroad and presently, from France, a government commission arrived for a demonstration. The year was 1913.

To the surprise of everyone except Leopold Salvator, the demonstration proved successful and the commission de-parted with assurances that an immediate offer would be forthcoming. The Frenchmen kept their word. Only two weeks later the Archduke Leopold Salvator held in hand a pledge for 1,000,000 gold francs.

The news brought consternation to Wachalowski & Com-pany.

Was it really true? Could a member of a ruling dynasty be endowed with commercial talents?

In haste Herr Wachalowski made a personal call on the Archduke, explaining that his firm still held the project under consideration. Surely His Imperial Highness would want to do the patriotic thing by keeping so brilliant an achievement within the borders of the fatherland?

Leopold Salvator smiled regretfully. He thought it more patriotic to play fair with France. Accordingly the patent

went to Paris. Not only this; the Archduke was already ne-
gotiating a second idea, namely the development of the caterpillar principle, enabling vehicles to run over unpaved and
difficult terrain. As yet he had merely looped long strips of
heavy sailcloth about the wheels of a small scout car, but
the initial experiment augured tremendous possibilities. This
time a British commission allied itself with the French in
viewing the demonstration, but, as had been the case with
Wachalowski, London manufacturers were skeptical when
informed that the inventor was a Habsburg prince.

Again France seized opportunity by the forelock. The
second patent was purchased by a leading tractor firm, which
would soon convert to manufacture of army tanks. But
Paris stole no march on the world. By that recurring coincidence, so often experienced in the field of invention, a
resourceful Briton emerged with caterpillar treads of native
metal and attached to battle wagons which preceded the
French product. London, not Paris, took credit for creation
of that lumbering monster, the first tank.

A third project launched by Leopold Salvator fared less
well. This was a device for rotating automobile headlights
at will.

Reception of this gadget was cool. It did not become immediately apparent why people should want to rotate their
headlights, and besides, the contrivance suffered from vibra-
tions and other defects in operation. Even so, a French pur-
chaser once more materialized, though at a modest price.
The principle was discarded by the automobile industry, but
successfuly applied in the manufacture of airport search-
lights.

The important point about all these enterprises was that,
on paper, Leopold Salvator had by his own efforts become a
wealthy businessman. There was only one drawback. Be-

fore the financial side of the above transactions had been
completed there was murder on a street in Sarajevo and the
First World War got off to a thunderous start. The patents
had reached Paris. But Leopold Salvator had as yet not seen
a red sou. . . .

Chapter Twelve

BECAUSE OF THEIR THRIFT the French as a nation have been held up to scorn and ridicule. Leopold Salvator was to find them scrupulously honorable in their acknowledgment of a debt. For, less than two years after the Armistice, the Paris Ministry of Finance—having learned the Archduke's whereabouts—made a first payment on the long-due royalties. Other instalments were to follow in the order agreed upon during those earlier 1913 negotiations.

These sums, though numerically impressive, no longer represented a sizable fortune. The franc, like most other European currency, had lost purchasing power and was destined to decline still further. But for the impecunious Austrians on Tibidabo Street any cash contribution was manna from heaven.

Actually it was Soledad who could be thanked for this. Her arrival had released Leopold Salvator from profitless domestic duties, permitting him to embark on worthier projects. As soon as he had laid aside the market basket, His Highness looked up a trustworthy Barcelona lawyer and through legal channels reopened contact with the Government of France. As a refugee from a defeated enemy country, he naturally expected no cordial reception; at best there might be prolonged litigation, with a compromise settlement in the end. At worst there would be nothing, and an attorney's fee for the pains.

It was a gamble one must take. In taking it, Leopold Salvator won back not only his faith in human character, but his own self-respect. For it had gnawed at his pride to be idle and financially adrift. The French funds, however modest, were neither charity nor a royal *apanage* coming to him by virtue of his birth; they were payment for honest work. In short, they restored recognition to him as head and provider for his family.

One immediate result of this happy windfall was the decision to move into more suitable quarters. The house on Tibidabo Street was in the vicinity of a noisy amusement park where crowds of Barcelona picnickers and their children spent week-end afternoons as well as all fiesta days. Calliope music, shouts, and the occasional echoes of a brawl drifted downhill, for the park was situated on the slope of Tibidabo Mountain and could be reached only on foot or by funicular tram. On Sundays this meant a constant flow of crowds with barkers circulating among them, until it seemed that concessionaires and their gaudy wares sprawled everywhere.

"I never know," sighed the Infanta Blanca, "when the snake man or the bearded lady will drop in to tea!"

The problem was solved as soon as the French funds arrived. Without loss of time another house was found, south of the city, in the suburb of Sarriá. Here too the background sloped toward the Barcelona Hills and Valvidrera Mountain (reached likewise by funicular) but there was no Luna Park or Coney Island touch. What was more, the new house, though inexpensive, had villa dimensions and was up for sale. With a reasonable down payment and monthly commitments to follow, the family could establish itself at least on a more stable footing.

"We ought to apply for Spanish citizenship," the Archduke Leopold Salvator proposed with a view to becoming a property holder. The thought brought joy and satisfaction to his wife, who had never ceased to be a Spaniard at heart.

Promptly this step too was initiated by sending a petition to the King, and thus avoiding needless delay.

Another direct result of their father's return to prosperity was a definite resumption of the children's education. Anton and the older girls, to be sure, were finished with ordinary schooling. But there was Dolores, handicapped by her lameness, who longed to take up drawing lessons. Immaculata, the pianist of the family, and Margareta, interested in dramatics and stage design, likewise hoped for a chance to further these talents. Maria Antonia and Assunta differed from the rest in that they had no concrete ambitions, which reflected in turn upon their characters. For, while their older sisters were always active and agog with plans, the two younger girls appeared listless and bored, seeking refuge in an exaggerated piety. They set up a routine of visiting churches in the most outlandish districts, where they remained from matins till vespers, perhaps less interested in devotions than in getting away from home. This was in part due to adolescent restlessness, though mostly, so their mother maintained, to an acute distaste for domestic duties.

Lastly, there were the two little ones—Franz Josef and Carlos—to be thought of. On Tibidabo Street, when funds were low, it had been decided that both boys must be enrolled in a cheap public school; in Spain these institutions were parochial in character, though subsidized by the government. Since even humbler middle-class families scorned free schooling as fit only for the poorest of the poor, the Infanta was greatly relieved at being able to make other plans. The boys were enrolled at the private academy of Bonanova, founded by St. Jean Baptiste de la Salle and run by lay monks known as the Hermanos de las Escuelas Cristianas.

At the last minute Carlos was scratched from the school

register, as the Infanta repented (Bonanova pupils were boarders) and kept her Benjamin at home.

"He is only ten," she excused her action, "and he's never been away!"

She would tutor Carlos herself, at least for another year, after which they could see what was to be done.

The incident engraved itself upon Franz Josef's mind, stabbing him to the quick. Again he must go off alone among strangers, away from home. Again his consciousness was pierced with the stinging realization that he had ceased to be the coddled one, the nestling, whom everyone loved. Always Carlos would be the Benjamin!

He felt unbearably forlorn. Also, from bitter experience at the Jesuit school of Feldkirch, he dreaded a return to monkish discipline. Already he could smell the mustiness of crowded dormitories, the stale refectory air, the bath shirts never dry from one dousing to another. . . . Still, at thought of the miseries endured at the Austrian monastery school he was warmed by a sudden access of optimism. Nothing could be so bad as the life he had known under the Jesuit rod; hence he need have no fear of Bonanova. Education being a necessary evil, he would brace himself and make the best of his present plight.

It was Papa who escorted Franz Josef to the new institute of learning. Papa always did all the unpleasant things, sparing Mama's sensibilities as well as occasional loss of face. The trip into town was made by tram, for the archducal affluence did not embrace a carriage or automobile. Between them father and son carried the satchel and small package holding Franz Josef's belongings.

The school lay in a narrow street halfway between Sarriá and the center of Barcelona proper. It was housed in a stone building, cold, dark, austere. The boy's jaw fell. Was there something about this forbidding exterior that recalled to him the dreary walls of Stella Matutina? But no, he must not think of that. The "Christian Brothers" were not Jesuits. At Bonanova everything would be different.

The formalities of admission were quickly disposed of and the time for parting had come. There seemed to be little to say. Papa swallowed once or twice, then resorted to the innocuous admonition:

"If you are a good boy, Pepi, there'll be a holiday at home in just a few weeks——"

Franz Josef was touched by the tenderness always present in his father's voice, but he was not fooled by promises of hypothetic holidays. Papa meant well, of course, and he perhaps even believed what he was saying. But Franz Josef did not believe it. He knew better. He had learned through hard experience that there was no compromise with monastic canons. Good behavior or bad had no bearing whatsoever on prescribed vacations, set stintingly for Christmas and a four-week interval in midsummer. He had not read Dante's *Inferno,* but in entering Bonanova he was "leaving all hope behind."

On Papa's departure a hooded dominie took the boy in hand, leading the way to the wardrobe department. Here Franz Josef was fitted with the dark striped apron, cut like a peasant smock, which all pupils wore over their clothes. In addition, his sailor suit, underwear and socks were marked in bright red thread with the number 194.

"We use no titles here," said the wardrobe master. "You will answer when your number is called."

As "194" Franz Josef went to bed that night in a dormitory shared with some fifty other boys of his age group, and, but for the fact that at the Stella Matutina all sleeping cots had been curtained off in separate cubicles, he might have been back at Feldkirch. The Hermanos Cristianos, he told himself resignedly, were going to be just like the Jesuits.

He was wrong. The sufferings he was to undergo at Bonanova made Feldkirch pale by comparison, for, while the Jesuit Fathers had been intellectuals who set great store by academic achievement, the "Christian Brothers" were ascetic extremists who despised the world and its vanities. The former applauded mental brilliance; the latter sought to crush it. At Bonanova everything except abject piety was sin.

Hygiene, for instance, was regarded with contempt. There were no bathrooms with showers or tubs: daily ablutions consisted of perfunctory face splashing (cold water) in a tiny hand basin. Though this was 1919, when all but the most primitive countries in the world regarded daily baths the rule rather than the exception, the "Christian Brothers" allowed only one weekly performance of so sybaritic a rite. Almost grudgingly the children were led to a basement chamber where they undressed and donned a gray long-sleeved tunic known as a bath shirt (the sight of the human body was another and particularly black sin). While they seated themselves on wooden benches along the walls, a bucket of warm water was passed around for a brief dipping of each boy's feet and, if desired, a trickling of soap suds under the folds of the bath shirt. In any case, immersion anywhere above the knees was an impossibility.

While this went on, the laundry supervisor of the school came to fetch the children's socks, which had collected in a malodorous pile outside the door. Clean socks were issued once a week, but a change of linens could not be looked forward to until the end of the month. Since the boys engaged in football and other active pastimes during recess, the odor of perspiration that exuded from them amounted to an evil fume. This was particularly noticeable at bedtime, when the unventilated dormitory was shut up for the night. The rancid smell of unclean humanity pervaded even the pillows and sheets.

For Franz Josef it was unbearable torture. He had a delicate nose, though even without this handicap the fetor would have proved trying, as attested to by boys of more rugged sensibilities.

"We all get sweaty feet here," a classmate confided, waving his toes in lamentable proof. "By Christmas you'll stink like a polecat!"

Franz Josef was appalled. He could not sleep for thinking of so horrible a prospect. Christmas! Papa and Mama waiting for him, and then perhaps pinching their noses (as he wanted to do right now in this abominable dormitory) because of the redolent foulness that surrounded his hapless person.

He remembered suddenly that Bonanova was considered an expensive school. His parents had not been able to send him there until that money came from Paris. But then something was wrong! Why should he not live as decently here as he did at home? Even in their poorest days, at Trieste, and on board ship during their flight from Genoa, Mama had insisted on the archducal linen being rinsed wherever there was access to soap and water. Surely she would not tolerate the swinish neglect to which he was exposed today!

He decided to do something about it. He wrote a letter home.

This was a mistake.

All correspondence went through the hands of the school prior, Brother Faustino, whom the more daring students nicknamed *El Tomate* ("The Tomato") because of his red face. Despite high blood pressure El Tomate was placid and good-tempered to the point of apathy, for his apoplectic body was bulwarked by great layers of paralyzing fat. The person to be feared as the real power behind the throne at Bonanova was the prior's assistant, Brother Saturnino, who taught the intermediate grades.

In Saturnino there was no trace of balmy torpor. Wiry, thin, with a hooked nose and raven hair, he bristled with vitality. He was a young lay monk, in his early twenties, yet he had attained impressive virtuosity as a disciplinarian. Saturnino punished as only a veteran in the art of flagellation could punish.

It was to this forbidding assistant that the prior turned over Franz Josef's letter. What followed did not count for only a single day, but for the duration of the Archduke's stay at Bonanova. "Number 194" had made a mortal enemy.

The immediate result was not only a public burning of the letter, to discourage other correspondents who might write in the same vein, but a savage beating at the hands of the expert castigator. Following this came the systematic persecution of the boy who was now pilloried as the grandson of Don Carlos, the late Pretender to the throne of Spain. A despicable Carlist, tolerated on Catalan soil only by Don Alfonso's generosity, dared to complain about the treatment he was getting! Let everyone spit upon this serpent in the grass, this ingrate and traitor!

At fourteen Franz Josef had not the stamina to meet malice without flinching. Though he was familiar with misfortune, it had not yet furnished him with a protective callousness toward fate's blows. At Bonanova these blows were actual, rather than figures of speech. In addition, he found himself the daily butt of Saturnino's venom, needled by sophistries such as:

"I suppose you deny being a descendant of the first Don Carlos?"

"No, sir——"

"There, he admits it! He has no shame!"

Next came the command to stand for hours facing a blank wall, with Brother Saturnino's eyes catching the slightest wavering motion. If the boy showed a trace of fatigue, and buckled in the knees or leaned his head against the wall, the monk was at his side, raining blows upon the defenseless victim's face.

Before many weeks Franz Josef no longer gagged at the stench in the school dormitory. As he wept himself to sleep he noticed that the merciless beatings so bruised his eyes, mouth and nose that he had lost all sensory perception beyond sheer, racking pain.

He was sorry, when he thought about it at all, that Papa had turned out such a good inventor. For without that money from France no admission to Bonanova would have been possible, and Franz Josef might still be at home with Carlos, learning his daily lessons from Mama.

Chapter Thirteen

IN THE HOUSE AT SARRIÁ, meanwhile, a different problem had arisen. While Franz Josef was thought excellently provided for, the Archduke Leopold Salvator and his wife found themselves with a new worry on their hands. It concerned their daughter Maria Antonia, whom the family called Mimi.

This young woman, now nearing twenty, was fast growing erratic in her religious pursuits. Her daily visits to Barcelona churches, in company of the much younger Assunta, had begun to create a sensation in clerical circles. There was capital to be drawn from such publicity.

"Look," parish priests pointed out to their flocks, "two princesses of the Imperial House of Austria choose to walk in the way of the Lord!"

Nuns smilingly stopped the archducal sisters on the street and urged them to visit the near-by Convento de las Teresianas, to inspire its members toward still greater consecration. . . . "We need new postulants," they hinted, not too obliquely. "God and His Church are best served by the voluntary abasement of those highly born——"

Finally Maria Antonia's confessor came right out with a direct probe. Did Her Highness not feel an overpowering vocation for the religious life? In ecclesiastic history there was mention of several queens who had reached beatification. But though Rome boasted many a royal saint, it still lacked one of imperial lineage.

All this was immensely flattering and far more agreeable to the ear than what Maria Antonia heard at home. For Mama had of late become a crank in the matter of ordering

her girls about and demanding that each fit herself for a
useful way of life. It was tiresome how critical Mama could
be, even about such trivial externals as the dressing of one's
hair. "Dowdy," she called it, when Maria Antonia dashed to
early Mass with yesterday's braids wound in straggles under
a deceptive mantilla. Yet Maria Antonia's "public" fawned
its adulation and interpreted such slovenliness as yet another
demonstration of her spirituality.

"She scorns adornment and carnal fripperies," they whispered, while Mama bluntly accused her daughter of being
lazy.

To cap this irritating state of affairs Maria Antonia came
home one day with the news that she would enter the novitiate at Tortosa, prior to taking the veil in the order of the
Teresianas.

Now it happened that both the Archduke Leopold Salvator and his wife were good Christians, brought up in the
Roman faith. They harbored no prejudice whatever against
the monastic life, nor did it seem to them unreasonable that
God should seek one of their brood of children for His service. But they could not believe that God could be so short-
sighted as to pick Maria Antonia. The thoughtful, limping
Dolores, yes; or Immaculata, with her deeply artistic and
musical soul. . . . But the other girls were made of worldier
stuff, hardly material for the cloistered life. . . .

Maria Antonia stood her ground. She wanted to be a nun.
Not only that: she wanted to go down in history beside the
Margravine Elisabeth and Queen Margit of Hungary, or
even Genevieve of Brabant, as the first imperial saint. If
thwarted, she might do something horrible to herself, like
jumping out the window or just pining away with despair.

There was nothing for the harassed parents to do but to
accede. They did so on one condition. Maria Antonia must

promise to go on a trip—any sort of trip—to get away from Barcelona influences, and to think things over before taking any irrevocable steps. The proposal was also intended to serve another end, namely to separate Maria Antonia from her younger sister Assunta, as the latter showed pronounced imitative tendencies and might at any moment duplicate the older girl's actions.

Surprisingly enough Maria Antonia took quite heartily to the idea of travel, proving her mother's contention that what looked like genuine religious ecstasy was often no more than an effort to escape from boredom. Of course, no far-flung Cook's Tour could be arranged for the eager young lady, since war-torn countries had as yet no tourist attractions to offer and in any case the family continued to live on a budget. But there was a weekly excursion boat to the Balearic Isles of Mallorca and Minorca where one might spend a pleasant and inexpensive vacation.

"Doesn't your Uncle Ludwig live there?" the Infanta Blanca asked her husband while the travel project was under discussion.

The Archduke reflected. Yes, come to think of it, long before the war there had been talk of a Habsburg renouncing all regal pomp, and settling among the fisher folk of Palma de Mallorca. In the family circle this rugged individualist was referred to as Uncle Baleares, but no one had bothered to keep contact with him or to ascertain whether indeed he was still there.

Uncle Baleares was something of a legend. He had been born as the Archduke Ludwig Salvator of Austria-Toscana, with the prerogatives and constrictions peculiar to his station. Early in life he was at cross purposes with dynastic dicta due to a violent infatuation with a Viennese of humble background.

The matter had reached the ears of the Emperor, who summoned Ludwig Salvator for a private inquiry. Was the young man involved in a routine flirtation or could there be truth in the rumor that he contemplated marriage?

"There is truth in the rumor, Sire," answered the Archduke.

At this His Majesty pronounced a familiar ultimatum, directed in its time at Ludwig's brother, Johann Orth, and other renegades who strayed from the imperial fold.

"Break with the girl—or drop your titles and leave the country!"

Ludwig Salvator had no trouble making up his mind. Shouldering a rucksack, he departed on the first train for Trieste and there boarded a ship heading into the Mediterranean. He had no plan or destination, but as the boat hove into the harbor of Palma the wanderer went ashore. For several months he inspected the sun-drenched islands which comprised an area of some two thousand square miles and a population of a quarter of a million souls. (This included the lesser known portion of the archipelago, the western islets of Iviza and Formentera.) In the end he returned to Mallorca and decided to make the small town of Palma his home.

Before long he was followed there by his Viennese sweetheart and it looked as though the story would climax in a happy ending. But the Emperor's ukase reached even to this far shore, though the Balearics were under Spanish rather than Austrian jurisdiction. Such was the catholicity of accord between Vienna and Madrid that no priest or civil clerk would marry the couple.

This predicament did not frustrate the erstwhile Archduke. Having salvaged substantial funds in several foreign banks, he now hired a personal secretary named Señor Vives, whose function it became to wed the young woman and live with her under the archducal roof, though not as her husband. At night, when the observing citizens of Palma had retired, roles were interchanged in Ludwig Salvator's hilltop house. The Archduke entered the boudoir while Señor Vives quietly betook himself to the master's bachelor quarters on the lower floor.

In time three sons and a daughter, all baptized under the patronymic of Vives, filled the happy abode. Ostensibly they were the children of the secretary, though in temperament and appearance they flagrantly belied the claim. Señor Vives was a dour, glum fellow of string-bean proportions, while his hypothetical offspring showed all the bounce and rosy bonhomie of their "godfather," the Archduke. However, with the passing years, wagging tongues grew tired and the situation lost its titillating novelty for the island population. Mallorcans accepted the strange ménage without cavil. After all, the world must be continuously repopulated. What did it matter who obligingly performed the trick?

It went without saying that the Barcelona Habsburgs were uninformed regarding the Balearic setup, or they would hardly have chosen Palma as a suitable place for Maria Antonia's spiritual reclamation. On his wife's advice Papa now sent a telegram to the almost legendary uncle, whom he had last seen in his youth, long before the war. The answer, signed by Señor Vives, was short and to the point:

"Archduke Ludwig Salvator dead."

"In that case," said the Infanta Blanca with characteristic feminine practicality, "there must be an inheritance. Perhaps you are an heir!"

Papa thought not. But he agreed that there was now an

Franz Josef as a child in gondola of his father's balloon "Meteor."

Archduke Franz Josef's Pilot License and Passport.

added reason for making the Mallorca trip. One ought at least to visit the grave of poor old Uncle Baleares.

By the next excursion boat the travelers set out, reaching the harbor of Palma after a short cruise. On arrival a surprise awaited them. The entire Vives clan stood at the pier, wreathed in smiles as sunny as their island. Uncle Baleares, they explained, had not yet been buried. He was packed away on ice.

"On ice?" The visitors were aghast.

Yes, he had been on ice at the morgue for many months, because no will had yet been found and the administrators did not know what to do with all the property.

All the property? The Infanta Blanca's brows arched significantly as she tried to catch her husband's eye. Just what was meant by this vague, though not unappealing, term?

It soon developed that the former imperial prince had become something of a patriarch in the islands. Dropping all pomp and pretense, he had gone native in a big way, consorting with the humblest fisherfolk and peasants. He even dressed and looked like a Mallorcan, wearing rope *espadrilles* and cotton trousers of rough weave. Yet despite this modest exterior, Uncle Baleares had done exceedingly well for himself. He owned fields, vineyards, houses, and even factory buildings in numbers not yet computed.

"Whenever the peasants needed money," one of the Vives boys explained, "they came and sold him something."

"Then there must be tenants on those properties," the Infanta inquired, "with a handsome yearly income accruing therefrom?"

No, Uncle Baleares had had no tenants and no income. He had just used up his Viennese inheritance by buying whatever the good Mallorcans had to sell, at whatever price they asked. Not because he wanted anything, but because they were his friends.

"What did he do with it all?" asked the unbelieving visitors.

"Nothing——"

"But surely the houses did not remain empty or the fields unplowed?"

"Oh, no! The original owners stayed right on. There was no place for them to go."

It developed that the local peasantry not only continued to operate and enjoy all the properties purchased from them by the erratic Habsburg, but at harvest time each year they sold him all their produce. What was more, they went fishing on his yacht (a neglected schooner, anchored in the harbor) and charged him fancy prices for their catch.

"I'm really a Communist at heart," Uncle Baleares was quoted as saying. "The island people have too little and I too much—so we make ends meet."

He had been a vegetarian too, which was just as well, in view of the mountains of broccoli, leek, endive, and finochio that were carted daily to his door. Since the practice still continued and the Vives household had no way of disposing of the stuff, vegetarianism became obligatory for its members in sheer self-defense.

The Infanta Blanca was not sure she approved.

To share the wealth by giving unto the poor was a fine Messianic precept, provided one remained wealthy and the poor were kept in their place. But Communism was another matter. There was something reprobate about the very word. It smacked of disorder and shoddiness, or unkempt hair or nails that were in need of trimming.

Come to think of it, the Vives family had photographs of Uncle Baleares, illustrating just what the Infanta meant. His locks seemed to have grown wild—and as for clothes, the Archduke must have worn anything and everything that tumbled from his cluttered cupboards.

"His Imperial Highness would tolerate no valet to keep things in order," explained Señor Vives.

Other idiosyncrasies came to light, such as Ludwig Salvator's travel methods. In preparing for a trip he would follow a system all his own: patiently he assembled on a table every piece of linen, toilet necessities, and other paraphernalia that were to go along. Next he pulled up a trunk alongside the table and, with one sweeping gesture of his arm, pushed the entire collection into its gaping depths.

"Packing," he boasted, "takes me exactly half a minute."

Uncle Baleares always carried an umbrella, a venerable object green with age, so worn at the tip that he had capped it with a brass thimble. Rain or shine, this umbrella had served him as a walking stick, a roof against sudden showers, or in dry weather as a shopping bag that expanded indefinitely with each added parcel.

On occasional visits to Paris, Ludwig Salvator was the despair of hotel and restaurant keepers, for he thwarted their every effort to make snobbish capital of his presence. If accompanied by a manservant, he would insist on the latter eating with him. This caused many a pained maître-d'hôtel to fetch a screen and hide the inelegantly democratic sight. Once, following a headwaiter's snub because the Balearic visitor and his companion were not formally attired, Ludwig Salvator laid down the menu and went back to his room where he and the servant donned white tie and tails. A moment later they returned downstairs, where they were received this time with bows and elaborate courtesies. The headwaiter himself ushered them to the most conspicuous and centrally located table.

"What will the order be, Your Imperial Highness?" he purred with satisfaction.

"Two cups of chocolate, please."

The man could not believe his ears, but Ludwig Salvator repeated the order quite succinctly. When the two cups were brought he and his companion emptied them over their starched bosoms and rose to go.

"There!" said Uncle Baleares in parting. "You were polite to us only because of our stiff shirts; well, that's all we think of them ourselves!"

On hearing such shocking anecdotes as the above it was the Infanta Blanca's considered opinion that her husband's relative must have been impossible.

Even so, the present Mallorca visit proved significant in more ways than one. Through concerted effort (in which the Barcelona guests lent a helpful hand) the home of the late Uncle Baleares was now turned upside down until each hidden niche and corner had been searched. And, in the end, the lost will was uncovered. It lay, slightly damp and musty from exposure, in the defunct Archduke's tackle box, beside his oilskin windbreaker, a crumpled beret, and a pair of redolent fishing pants.

If outwardly the humid document was no nosegay, its contents likewise proved hardly a matter for rejoicing, at least so far as Habsburg kin were concerned. For Uncle Baleares bequeathed all his earthly effects to the four Vives children, who at the will's reading were fully grown and even approaching middle age.

The disclosure was received with genuine surprise. Quite obviously the favored heirs thought of their benefactor simply as a devoted *padrino* (godfather) rather than a true progenitor. Or were they artfully concealing their knowledge of early gossip concerning the triangle that once had kept all Mallorca in a delightful pother?

In any case, the Infanta Blanca was forced to admit that once again her husband had been right. No pot of gold awaited him in the fair town of Palma. Neither his name nor that of any other Habsburg had been mentioned in the will.

Perhaps because of this, or because they were hedonists who had no use for fusty reading matter, the Vives clan offered to give up their *padrino's* library. During off hours Uncle Baleares, it developed, had been something of a scholar. Like the Prince of Monaco, he enjoyed a reputation as an authority on crustaceans and other forms of marine life. He had also written a number of treatises on botany, specializing in the study of medicinal herbs. But perhaps most valuable to his own imperial kin were Ludwig Salvator's researches into ancient dynastic lore.

For one thing, he had traced back the uniquely Austrian title of "archduke" to the year 953 A.D., when one Duke Bruno of Lorraine became Archbishop of Cologne and decided to flaunt his new ecclesiastic rank in conjunction with his worldlier and more modest nomenclature. To this end he devised the Latin combination *Archidux*. The Greek root of *archaios* meant "old, archaic, revered," hence implied excellency and pre-eminence above even the Russian title of "grand duke" or the positively commonplace "prince," particularly as both the latter lacked the religious cachet so dear to the very Catholic House of Austria.

Though heraldic statutes did not at first recognize the hybrid appellation, there was an Abbot Rudolph of Habsburg in 1138, and a Palatine Duke Rudolph IV in 1365, both calling themselves *Archiduces Palatii* or Principal Dukes of the Court. The odd title implanted itself through use and was

finally confirmed. Centuries later, when Austria's great
Empress Maria Theresia married Francis of Lorraine, archdukes and archduchesses enjoyed their most spectacular
prestige.

In addition to such general information, Uncle Baleares
had made many notations regarding the Habsburg-Toscana
line, and in particular the branch carrying the name Salvator, his own. During the reign of the same Maria Theresia,
the Tuscan Grand-Ducal House of Medici had died out with
the childless Giovan Gastone, following which the Austrian
Empress negotiated a treaty whereby her son Franz was to
act as governing Grand Duke. On her own death he was
recalled to ascend the Austrian throne as Emperor Franz II,
while his brother Leopold became Grand Duke and fathered
a long Tuscany line. As prolific descendants again and
again were baptized with the name of their common an-
cestor, *Babbo Leopoldo,* "Papa Leopold," it became necessary to distinguish among them. Thus the cadet branch of
Salvator started. Altogether the Tuscan Habsburgs flourished until 1861 when, with Cavour's unification of Italy,
their rule ended.

As a minor study Uncle Baleares had made a few notations that came under the heading of family gossip. Perhaps
due to the unconventional course his own life had followed,
he seemingly had taken pleasure in listing all those reckless
Habsburgs who broke with tradition to sacrifice title and
embark upon their own romantic ways. Among these was
his younger brother, known to the world as Johann Orth,
whose disappearance in the South Atlantic on the schooner
Margherita (with a girl named Milli Strubl) remains a matter of conjecture. Next, there was Leopold Ferdinand of
Toscana, renaming himself Leopold Woelfling so as to
marry plain Fräulein Clara Pavlovska, while his sister Luise

(wife of the Crown Prince of Saxony) eloped with the violinist Enrico Toselli. Lastly the Archduke Ferdinand Karl, brother of Franz Ferdinand (Sarajevo) and of Handsome Otto (*Le Beau*), chose to live as a simple Professor Ferdinand Burg in happy marriage with a colleague's daughter, Berta Czuber.

Needless to say, these matters were of no interest whatever to the Vives offspring. Magnanimously they inquired whether the Barcelona Habsburgs wanted Uncle Ludwig Salvator's vast store of manuscripts and books.

It was the sort of offer that could not be decently turned down. With a sigh and a quick mental estimate of probable shipping expenses the Infanta Blanca nodded to her husband. He made a polite acceptance speech.

Up to now the Balearic journey had certainly been a total loss.

Chapter Fourteen

IN QUITE ANOTHER WAY Palma de Mallorca prepared for the visitors a most agreeable surprise: the Archduchess Maria Antonia found a suitor in the person of one Ramón de Orlandis y Villalonga, whose father had been a marquis. In the Balearic Isles titles of nobility remained in force only so long as a tax was collected by the authorities for their use. The elder Orlandis had let his payments lapse, hence Ramón was unencumbered by rank. He also was not wealthy. But he had Byronic features and a romantic air, which radically changed Maria Antonia's mind about entering the convent. Instead, she fell heels over head in love.

"I knew it," said the Infanta Blanca. "The only veil our Mimi really wants to wear is that of a bride!"

The suitor's humble station was not allowed to hamper romance, for times had changed and royalty could not be choosers. Besides, the Archduke and his wife would rather have seen their daughter married to the lowliest island planter than buried in a nunnery somewhere in Spain. They heartily blessed the match.

The engagement was celebrated under the Vives roof, with characteristic Vives conviviality and an abundance of heady Mallorcan wine. Unmindful of her erstwhile longing for eternal chastity, Maria Antonia radiated happiness. She wanted to remain at Palma and marry at once. But there was the matter of Ramón's finances; the young man needed to be more firmly established in the business world before taking on the responsibility of a wife and home. Tearfully Maria Antonia prepared to accompany her parents back to Spain.

At Barcelona the telegraphed news of the Balearic romance was received with mixed feelings. The older archduchesses, Dolores, Immaculata, and Margareta, were greatly diverted at their sister's radical recovery from her pietistic seizure. A fine nun that giddy Maria Antonia would have made, if she could be swept off her feet at her first encounter with temptation! Just wait till the minx got home again: she would be subjected to unmerciful taunts and heckling.

One person alone in the archducal household did not join in the laughter. This was Assunta, youngest of the girls, and the one who had most feverishly emulated Maria Antonia's supposed sanctimony.

To Assunta the news of the Mallorcan betrothal came as a sharp blow. She saw no humor in the shameless reversal of Maria Antonia's position. Far from being amused, Assunta was profoundly shocked.

It is not impossible that she may also have been a trifle jealous. Of all the sisters, Mimi had been her favorite, because nearest her own age—though a shade prettier. Sentiment might be blended here with subconscious rivalry. There was no question but that Mimi's heart belonged now to another: a man, with whom even the most devoted of sisters could not compete. But there was a second and more rankling thought. It had been simple enough to parrot the older girl's protestations about religious vocation and the pledging of monastic vows. What now? Would it be as easy for Assunta (who, after all, had not been taken on a pleasure voyage) to follow suit and likewise catch herself a beau?

She was sorely plagued by the dilemma. Her seventeen-year-old mind wrestled with two doubtful alternatives: should she stand by her guns or, like Maria Antonia, become a renegade? The former choice involved no hazard and it was certain to earn her a crown in heaven, not to mention the sensation it might create right here on earth. As for the second alternative, there was always the possibility of failure and winding up (disastrous thought) as an old maid.

In the end her piety won the day.

She, Assunta, was not like the others. She had will power and a mind of her own. Let them mock Maria Antonia whose actions had invited ridicule; Assunta was not play-acting. She would show them that she was in deadly earnest.

Her resolution received further impetus through the Teresianas, whom she now visited alone and with renewed fervor. The nuns were careful not to stint with plaudits for one so rooted in the ways of the Lord.

"Alas," they tactfully deplored the defection of Maria Antonia, "that misguided young woman was a victim of self-delusion!"

They sought to interpret the Balearic romance as a mirage contrived by heavenly design so that the younger sister's true calling might be the more clearly manifested. By contrast, Assunta's inner voices had the ring of authority. Her vocation was no pseudo-visionary alarum: it was the real thing.

So firmly did Assunta believe this herself that she soon hardly left the convent to come home to sleep. She begged the nuns to let her help in the sacristy or kitchens, where she performed menial tasks that would accrue to her soul's salvation. If the same duties had been required of her in the house at Sarriá, she would doubtless have found them less beatific. At home there was also a pronounced lack of appreciation, as no one exclaimed:

"How wonderful—an archduchess peeling onions like the

humblest drudge!" Or else: "The daughter of royalty stoops to scrub floors!"

Her performance garnered praise and publicity that might well have aroused the envy of a prima ballerina or an opera star. She was by way of becoming a celebrity, since all the attention formerly divided between Mimi and herself was concentrated now upon Assunta alone.

It happened that the Teresianas did not accept postulants at the parent order in Barcelona, and in any case the Archduchess was a minor who could not be enrolled without sponsorship by a responsible guardian. But this did not prevent the pious sisterhood from fanning the divine spark and guiding it in the right direction, namely the novitiate at Tortosa, where Maria Antonia had once wanted to go. Indeed, by the time her parents returned from their Balearic holiday, Assunta was past management. The confusion of the family reunion became the setting for a private drama of her own.

There had been talk at the Teresianas concerning two nuns who were going overseas to open a new convent in South America. Their sailing date coincided with the hullabaloo attendant upon Maria Antonia's arrival and further celebration of the engagement. Well, Assunta would not be there. She was going to the docks to bid farewell to the departing nuns. Following some intuitive warning, Mama decided at the last minute to accompany her youngest daughter on this errand.

The ship chosen by the Teresianas was an Italian liner of modest tonnage and unheralded name. But it was big enough for a girl to hide in its bowels, in defiance of the most rigorous search. And this was exactly what happened. While her mother talked politely with the two nuns, Assunta disappeared suddenly from the docks. She slipped up the gangplank without hat, coat, or baggage (it was part of her religious obsession to dress like a pauper) and remained out of sight till the ship gave a parting toot and pulled up anchor.

On discovering her daughter's absence, the Infanta spread an immediate alarm. The ship was held up forty minutes past sailing time, but a quick inspection netted no stowaway aboard.

"She must have gone back to the convent," concluded Mama. "That girl is utterly unpredictable!"

At home in Sarriá, meanwhile, the excitement and to-do about Mimi's betrothal had subsided. As the household quieted down and dusk began to fall it was observed that Assunta had still not returned. Soledad was sent forthwith to the nunnery with orders to fetch the Archduchess home. But the Teresianas likewise had seen no trace of their young friend since she had left for the docks early that morning. Could some accident have befallen her? Might she be lying even now, beaten and ravished, in some dark Barcelona street?

Panic seized the household at Sarriá. Instantly the family divided into searching parties which would comb the neighborhood, while Papa and Anton raced downtown to the police. Throughout that night the alarm spread into every precinct, including the outermost suburbs. It was not until morning that the Infanta Blanca voiced a firm conclusion:

"She must be on that boat——"

In person the Archduke Leopold Salvator called at the shipping offices and the Italian Consulate General. From here on the matter assumed official character as wires were exchanged with Rome, the Foreign Office, and King Victor Emmanuel himself.

The Italians responded gallantly. *"Faremmo lo possibile,"* they promised. They would do what they could.

The ship had long passed Gibraltar and was nosing into mid-Atlantic when her skipper received wireless orders to stage a minute inspection from bow to stern. Even at the risk of violating passenger privacy, not a square inch of shipping space must be overlooked. This meant that the cabin of the traveling nuns, heretofore held inviolate, would undergo sharp scrutiny. Despite virtuous protest, the holy ladies were bidden to unlock their trunks and closets, and to permit a peep under the beds.

Threatened with such rude intrusion, the Teresianas gave up their secret. From under their wing the Archduchess Assunta emerged suddenly on deck.

She looked rosy and well fed, for the good sisters had discreetly foraged among dining-room leftovers for tidbits to sustain their hidden charge.

"We pray late at night," they had told the steward, who readily understood the weakening effect of devotions in the wee small hours. In consequence he had furnished them cold cutlets, fruits, and an occasional assortment of *petits-fours*. Assunta fattened and flourished noticeably under such good treatment; she faced the world in happy unconcern when at last the game was up. In fact, she was rather glad to get some fresh air.

Her appearance created a sensation among the other passengers. To think that an imperial princess had been hiding all this time right in their midst! So pretty, and modest too —why, she had not even a hat or coat, or a single change of dress! She had left behind all thought of vanity and worldly pomp, in order to follow her true vocation as a nun. . . .

It was wonderful. Fellow travelers gazed in rapture at the young girl, as though she were another Saint Thérèse de Lisieux or Bernadette Soubirous, destined for some glorious revelation. Not a single critic ventured to censure the runaway daughter, whose thoughtlessness had caused her distraught parents untold anguish, not to mention the expense and international confusion occasioned by the search. Assunta had become a heroine; she was the star in a play staged and directed exclusively by herself. Nor did she lack an appreciative audience. The whole ship became her doting public.

Within a matter of minutes a committee had been formed to solicit clothes and toiletries for the "destitute" stowaway. Soon the Archduchess was decked out in finery which, if it did not exactly suit an incipient bride of Christ, made her look very chic indeed. With the raiment suddenly at her disposal the would-be nun could easily have become a protagonist in a daily fashion show.

The question remained: what was to be done, now that the lost Archduchess had been found? For hours the ship's radio operator remained in contact with Barcelona and Rome, awaiting instructions. Was the South American cruise to be cut short, while the imperial stowaway returned to her parents? Or would the latter relent and allow fate to take its course?

Actually neither alternative prevailed. The owners of the shipping line could not afford to jeopardize their commitments by changing the vessel's course, nor would the majority of the passengers (regardless of their admiration for Assunta) have tolerated any tampering with their travel schedules. On the other hand, the Archduke Leopold Salvator and his wife had no intention of letting their self-willed daughter off too easily. Assunta was still a minor. As such she could be held by port authorities wherever the ship dropped anchor, and returned to her parents by the next

Europe-bound liner. It was not a question of blind intolerance or unfair restraint; no one had forbidden Assunta to
become a nun. But if she did persist in her desire, after reasonable reflection and the attainment of her majority, she
might do so without inciting an international scandal. This
much Papa and Mama thought they had a right to ask.

The skipper received orders from Rome. He was to take
the Archduchess to Buenos Aires, where she would be put
under arrest and spirited to the Italian Embassy. Her de-
tention was of course a mere technicality, since she would be
the personal guest of Rome's envoy, Pietro Badoglio, head-
line figure of World War II.

Assunta did not take any of this to heart. She enjoyed
her escapade immensely, squeezing out of it each ounce of
novelty and adventure. The sea voyage in itself had been
gloriously exhilarating. Now, on Argentine soil, she inveigled the embassy personnel to take her sightseeing, mind-
ful all the time that she was their helpless and docile
prisoner. Needless to say, in Buenos Aires too she became
the target of all eyes, as the news soon got around concerning her romantic flight. The South American spree
ended as a personal triumph.

Eventually, however, time caught up with the fair runaway. Less than a week after landing she found herself once
more aboard ship, heading back for Spain.

The return voyage was not nearly so stimulating as the
triumphal progress that had preceded it. To begin with, the
vessel was no luxury liner or even a packet boat, but a humble freighter with only a few passengers for cargo. As she
had formerly been in East Indian service, her hull was designed for Pacific waters, ill-suited to the choppy wave
length of the Atlantic. The travelers, such as Assunta could
count during her own infrequent appearances on deck, were

knocked about unmercifully. No, this time she was quite without a public. She had not even the two Teresianas standing helpfully in the wings and whispering their cues.

In short, the journey back was a dismal bore. Assunta spent it listlessly at a conventual pastime, making bobbin lace.

Chapter Fifteen

SHE REACHED BARCELONA considerably chastened. The dreary weeks aboard the freighter, minus the pleasures and distractions to which she had grown accustomed during the earlier trip, led her to brooding and introspection. For a time she saw herself as a picturesque martyr, hunted by cruel pursuers. But presently these not unalluring visions gave way to simple pangs of conscience. She knew she was in for a sound dressing-down.

As the ship docked it was a meek and contrite Assunta who stepped ashore.

It cannot be said that she was received with open arms. Her mother and father had been too deeply aggravated for that. But the lost sheep was quietly led back into the fold and given time to get her bearings, before being called to task for her misdemeanor.

The curtain lecture, when it came, carried a punch. Both Papa and Mama were voluble when in a temper, and they had never been caught short in the matter of vocabulary. Assunta was told off in emphatic terms that godliness begins at home and that a disregard of filial duty is no way to feather a nest in heaven. In short, until she was twenty-one she would be expected to adjust herself to obedience and family responsibility, like her brothers and sisters. After that she would be free to do whatever she pleased.

The tempest over, there were kisses and embraces, while the girl tearfully promised to mend her ways. Harmony returned at last to the sorely tried household at Sarriá.

It was not for long.

A week after these events, as a neighborhood seamstress

arrived for the planning of Maria Antonia's trousseau, the garden gate was found ajar. It was early morning and no one had been heard to exit, though the iron hinges protested dolefully against the slightest move. The key hung on its customary hook inside the garden wall. Had someone forgotten to lock up last night?

The mystery was quickly solved. One day a week each of the girls had been charged with full responsibility for the household keys. After her overseas escapade Assunta was quietly reinstated in the fold, and only yesterday marked her first turn at the homely routine.

She took full advantage of it, for it now developed that the fanatical girl had once more disappeared. She was nowhere on the premises, and inspection of her room disclosed that the bed had not been slept in.

"Well," said the Infanta Blanca resignedly, "there's no doubt about it this time. She really means it."

No effort was made to revive the earlier commotion by calling on foreign diplomats or even the local police. Wherever Assunta had gone, her parents did not propose spreading another transatlantic dragnet to force her return. They faced the simple fact that she had stepped out of their lives, this time for good.

Oddly, inaction proved more effective than hysterical alarms. As soon as no one bothered to solve the secret of her whereabouts, Assunta was heard from. She volunteered the information that she had entered the novitiate at Tortosa, the coastal town south of Barcelona on the sea route to Valencia. Though not of age, she hoped to get a special dispensation from the Pope, permitting her formal registration without parental consent.

Archduke Leopold Salvator and his wife saw no need for further headlines or melodrama. They assured Assunta of their full agreement and blessings. Also, they would be much obliged if she left the Pope alone.

By coincidence there lived in Tortosa an old priest named Father Domingo, who read mass for the novices, and on special feast days preached at the monastery school of Bonanova in Barcelona. Here he soon learned that student "194" was a brother of the now celebrated Archduchess Assunta who had brought such prestige to the Teresianas. He wondered, not illogically, whether God's call might not be stirring likewise in the boy. Perhaps something ought to be done about this?

Father Domingo was a gentle and saintly man, as valuable to the Church as the sadistic Saturnino was detrimental. From the start Franz Josef had warmed to the gray-haired priest, though not to the extent of confiding in him regarding his own sufferings. But during Easter Week the boy accompanied Father Domingo to Tortosa for a brief visit with Assunta. It was the priest's secret hope that the young Archduke might be inspired by his sister's noble example. What a triumph it would be if an imperial prince could be induced to enter the service of the Lord! Ordinarily the Church found its recruits among the lowlier classes, though royalty was conspicuously represented by the current House of Saxony. But an ordained Habsburg was something else again.

"You could one day become cardinal," said Father Domingo in a visionary mood.

Franz Josef, despite his rigorous clerical education, had no firm grasp on matters of ecclesiastic rank, though Father Domingo's tone indicated that cardinals came very high indeed. Even so, he felt not the slightest inclination to become part of a hierarchy that could harbor the ruthless Saturnino among its members. He was himself a devout

Catholic, but he did not think Saturnino represented true Catholicism or even the most elementary teaching of Christ. The monkish cassock no less than the hero's gold braid could disguise a tyrant heart.

Father Domingo was unaware of the strong resistance built up in Franz Josef's mind. Realizing the power of dramatic ritual, he required the boy to serve as *monaguillo* (acolyte) at Mass in his Tortosa parish church. To ring the sacring bell and swing a censer was a thrill to any youth. Actually the Archduke spoke his Latin responses and performed his duties with great zest, but he still did not want to be a cardinal. He wanted to be an aviator.

The good priest had not shot his final arrow. There was yet the confrontation between Franz Josef and Assunta. When brother and sister came face to face the heavenly call might well transmit itself from one to the other, as was recorded so traditionally in the saints' lives. One must proceed with patience, and a grain of caution.

It was Maundy Thursday when at last the young Archduke and Archduchess met in the conventual visitors' room. Assunta already wore the garb of an accepted novice, though her hair had not been cut and she was without coif or veil. These adjuncts marked only the fully consecrated nun.

Conversation lagged between brother and sister until Franz Josef noticed the unbuttoned cuff of Assunta's left sleeve. The pale skin of her wrist seemed to have turned an angry red.

"What's the matter with your arm?" he asked in sudden dread. Could there be a female Saturnino in this nunnery, who flogged her victims with all the savagery of her Bonanova counterpart? The thought of a girl receiving the same castigations under which he himself still suffered caused a shudder to run down his back.

But there was nothing in Assunta's contented face to indicate that she had undergone abusive treatment. On the contrary, she seemed to have anticipated his question, for she now rolled up her sleeve and exposed the length of her lower arm which, at a quick glance, appeared to be a single expanse of badly scarred flesh.

"Look!" she beamed in a tone of challenge. "Now can anybody doubt my vocation?"

He thought at first that she had been marked by divine stigmata, since nothing else could explain the exaltation in her blazing eyes. But her next words cleared up his error.

"I did it myself," she said proudly, "with a knife heated in a flame——"

He shrank back, yet could not refrain from looking again. This time his eyes discerned two sharply etched characters that had been carved into the scorched flesh; they were the initials "J" and "M," each followed by a series of inflamed blotches.

"They spell out Jesus and Mary," Assunta elucidated.

In his stupefaction he blurted out an almost flippant question. "Where's Joseph?"

She assumed a deadly seriousness. "Joseph was a human being, and a man. You don't seem to realize that I am through with men forever!"

This was certainly conclusive. Whether by her extraordinary act Assunta meant once and for all to annihilate her family's skepticism, or whether her self-maceration gave proof of genuine religious transport, one thing seemed clear. The young woman had made up her mind. There was no further room for suasion.

Franz Josef could not help being impressed, the more so

as Father Domingo and the prioress of Tortosa vied with each other in singing Assunta's praises.

"*Qué santa! Qué pura!*" they intoned, ecstatically. "How saintly! How pure!"

The whole convent made full capital of the name, Maria Assunta, which signified the Assumption or Ascension into Heaven of the Holy Mother. Franz Josef vaguely spotted a touch of oratory in the encomiums, perhaps in the intonation or the well-practiced rhythm. Having served as an acolyte since earliest childhood, he knew the Latin liturgy by heart. The shower of compliments, though Spanish, seemed reminiscent to him of the *Salve Regina:*

> "*O Clemens, O Pia,*
> *O Dulcis Virgo Maria!*"

Had Assunta not been his own sister, whose every facial expression he could recognize and instinctively interpret, she would have seemed to him now disembodied and no longer of this earth. The vestal quality enveloped her as completely as though she already wore the hood of a praying Beguine, one of those chanting West Indian nuns who sway during their orisons. The comparison was not farfetched, for Assunta glowed with the zeal of a whirling dervish. Still, behind the aureole of holiness that was being spun so subtly about her, Franz Josef discerned the earthy girl whom no one at Tortosa really knew. He thought he understood also the lure which all this concentrated attention had for her. Was she not, like himself, one of ten children, forever lost in the collectiveness that ruled an oversized nursery? Had they ever been individuals? He well knew that at times Mama could not remember the exact birthdays of her numerous offspring; and, though she loved them, there was a certain diffuse collectivism even about that love.

Assunta must have felt it too. Her fierce rebellion against being a mere decimal had long kept the family in an uproar. He recalled that time in Vienna, when King Nikita of Montenegro came on a visit to Schönbrunn, and by imperial command the entire Habsburg clan had been summoned to appear.

Papa, Mama, and their flock (Carlos had not yet been born) arrived in their best bibs and tuckers, to be presented to the comic-opera king. Nikita was a mountaineer of peasant stock, who ruled over a speck of land called Czernagora (Black Mountain), and whose lapses in etiquette made anecdoctal history. He adored children, having two sons and five beautiful daughters of his own. During recurrent visits to prolific Austria he liked to check up on vital statistics.

As the Leopold Salvator brood lined up before him, the Balkan monarch kissed each child on both cheeks and cried expansively:

"What would you like for a present?"

This created a dilemma, as there had been previous and stern parental instructions not to take advantage of such courtesy. But Nikita meant what he said. While the young archdukes and archduchesses stood tongue-tied, he reached into his pockets and pulled forth a medal, a brooch, a jeweled ring. However, there were more Habsburgs than he had bargained for. By the time Assunta and her younger brother stood in line (their cousins, the Valerie children, had preceded them) Nikita ran out of gifts. He had nothing left but promises. Turning to the Archduke Pepi, he said:

"For you, my lad, the best tailor in Cetinje will make a guardsman's uniform!"

The child swallowed a request he had been bursting to make. There stood behind Nikita a giant equerry holding a tray of cigarettes and a tall lighted candle; his day-long job consisted of keeping the King, who was a chain smoker, constantly supplied. This equerry had captured the Archduke Pepi's imagination. Instead of a guardsman's uniform the small Franz Josef wanted nothing so much as a try at one of Nikita's cigarettes.

The Montenegrin monarch had meanwhile spotted Assunta, who offered her best curtsy. She was an appealing little girl at whose sight Nikita regretted having no more trinkets. But there were his boys, Danilo and Pjetr, reaching marriageable age: it would not hurt to keep an eye on this pert miss as a prospective daughter-in-law. Kissing Assunta's hand, the portly ruler exclaimed:

"Never have I seen a lovelier princess! How would you like to become Queen of Montenegro?"

Actually, as heirs to the smallest throne in Europe, Nikita's sons would not have easy pickings for consorts. The bombastic compliment tossed at the eight-year-old girl was an oblique hint to be noted and weighed by her elders.

To Assunta only the words "Queen of Montenegro" had held significance. She saw the rotund and amiable Balkan potentate as a story-book Lord Bountiful who was going to give her a kingdom.

"I am the Queen of Montenegro!" she prattled to the servants at Wilhelminenberg after the Vienna visit had ended. "I'll have a crown and scepter and castle of my own——"

This resulted in considerable spoofing by her older brothers and sisters who, at night, gathered about Assunta's bed and dropped on their knees in mock obeisance.

"Never have we seen a sillier princess!" they screamed in hysterics. "How would you like to be Queen of the Ashcan?"

Assunta bore their taunts with dignity. In her own fancy

she was still King Nikita's elect, while young Anton and Franz Josef were her pages. For, soon after his departure, the Balkan monarch had sent two miniature guardsmen's uniforms with shiny buttons for both lads. Decked out in such elegance, they consented to enter into Assunta's game.

Today, more than ten years later, Franz Josef watched this same sister garnering the homage and adulation of the nuns and parishioners of Tortosa, and he could not help wondering whether she might still be playing Queen of Montenegro. Always Assunta's yearning to stand out as an individual had made her hunger for attention. She loved praise. Like every lonely child, she blossomed under it.

He might be wrong, of course. The girl who seemed to him so familiar might be a stranger after all. Even in her present garb of a novice there was something about her that ran true to form, but he could be mistaken. The long history of Christian saints abounded with instances where those nearest of kin failed to recognize the light shining in their midst. Perhaps Assunta was such a light?

To keep on the safe side and refrain from unwitting blasphemy, he preferred to reserve judgment. There was, after all, Father Domingo's verdict, brooking no contradiction:

"*Qué santa! Qué pura! María Assunta——*"

It was almost funny, when he thought of the pig-tailed sister whose hair ribbons he had pulled, and who in turn had administered those ineffectual thrashings that merely spurred him on to further devilment.

Well, they moved now in different worlds. But one thing was clear. Notwithstanding Assunta's passport into Heaven, he, the Archduke Pepi, had no desire to accompany her there.

The tonsure and the cloth were not for him.

Chapter Sixteen

THE TORTOSA VISIT, undertaken in the spirit of a pilgrimage, could be put down as a failure.

At Bonanova no bed of roses awaited Franz Josef when it became known that his saintly sister's example did not prompt him to follow in her path. Though Father Domingo showed neither resentment nor vindictiveness, the hostility nursed by Brother Saturnino seemed to have redoubled. This was partly Franz Josef's own fault. Or rather, it was the result of some dangerous advice imparted to him while his parents had sojourned in Mallorca.

During that Balearic interlude the girl Soledad had been charged with full household responsibilities, including periodic visits to Bonanova to keep track of the Archduke Pepi's needs. On the occasion of her first call she had been bidden to sit in the reception room while someone went to fetch the boy. It was a long wait, and when Franz Josef at last appeared she had trouble recognizing him. He had had that very day an especially rough encounter with Saturnino, as a result of which his face was puffed and distorted from brutal cuffings. In addition, he was cowed and frightened, unwilling to meet his caller.

Soledad had difficulty getting him to speak. When he finally did so, it was only in whispers, lest the walls have ears. He spoke haltingly of his sufferings, while tears ran down his sore cheeks. In the end he nerved himself to implore Soledad for help.

"Tell Papa to come here and take me away," he begged.

She promised to do what she could. But the Archduke Leopold Salvator and his wife had written from Palma that they planned to extend their stay (this was during the blossoming of Antonia's romance). What if they did not return for another month?

"There's just one thing to do, Your Highness," said Soledad. "Get yourself expelled!"

"But how?"

"Get tough and forget all that rot about holding up the other cheek. Disobey orders, break up discipline in the classroom, become such a nuisance that they will want to be rid of you——"

He stared at her hopefully. "You really think that will help?"

"It's the only way to fight against tyranny. Break up the pattern, disrupt the clockworks. A bully plots his cruelties systematically, so one must harass and disorganize him."

There was not much time for Soledad to get specific, but Franz Josef followed the general drift of her advice.

He let down in his schoolwork and became recalcitrant when called to task. During classes he incited fellow students to porcine squeals or catcalls, and altogether set discipline on its ear.

This by no means improved his lot. Brother Saturnino's fury reached white heat as the persecutions were intensified. Franz Josef's sufferings grew worse. Whatever knowledge of psychology Soledad had gleaned at the orphanage of Santa Brígida, it certainly did not seem to fit Bonanova.

Father Domingo's selection of an acolyte for Easter services in Tortosa had brought a brief respite. But for Franz Josef it was only a fancied escape. He knew in his heart that on returning to the orbit of his enemy there would be still greater terrors to endure. The knowledge that he, a Bonanova charge, had openly repudiated the priesthood as a prospective career was bound to cause unfavorable comment. Saturnino would make the most of it.

In his extremity Franz Josef now hit upon a desperate plan. Heretofore his pranks and misdemeanors had been directed solely at his tormentor. But, after all, Saturnino himself was only an insignificant cog in what Soledad had called the "clockworks." Tempests in teapots were ineffective. One must create a storm where it would do some good. In short, he resolved to stir up a large-scale riot against El Tomate, the fat Prefect.

On Sunday mornings The Tomato appeared for convocation exercises, following which each student was allowed to address one single remark to him, either in the form of a question or a complaint. Here was Franz Josef's chance. After days and nights of secret coaching he had enlisted some two dozen classmates for a concerted attack. When The Tomato rose next Sunday to open the "consultation period" they were to shout one single question at his head:

"Why does the directive board of Bonanova break the civil law of Spain, which forbids beating children in the schools?"

Two dozen voices would not have made much of a showing, but on the appointed day the chorus had swelled to a hundred, as new recruits were won hourly to the cause. This was the more extraordinary in view of the cowed spirit prevailing generally among the boys, all of whom had hardships to endure. It required courage of a high order to rise in helplessness and speak for justice. But the feat was accomplished. The convocation exercises ended in an uproar.

The immediate result was a collapse suffered by The Tomato, who was carried off the rostrum with glazed eyes and a purple face. The clergy did not like to tangle with civil authority, hence the reaction on the part of the school heads was fear that student complaints had reached the outside world, an almost unthinkable possibility in view of the strict censorship.

For a few days there was cautious suspense, while each classroom became the scene of an exhaustive inquisition. As the teaching body became convinced however that the rebellion was purely childish in character, with no official reverberations from the police, there was hell to pay. Who was the culprit at the bottom of so brazen a conspiracy? The entire school would be put on rations of bread and water until the guilty one had been ferreted out.

No traitor arose to denounce Franz Josef, for he was loved among his classroom and dormitory companions. But by a simple process of elimination the sharp inquisitors fixed finally upon his name. Perhaps it was the very kindness of his friends which turned the trick; no other student was so noticeably shielded and praised by his fellows as the Archduke, hence he came under direct suspicion. It was a case of "protesting too much."

Brother Saturnino all but girded his loins for action. With the flaming wrath of an avenging demon he concentrated on a fitting punishment. But before he could lay hands on his victim the school board interfered. El Tomate had arrived at the decision to send Franz Josef home as an undesirable student. Lest the boy blacken the school's reputation by making detrimental revelations, his expulsion from Bonanova would be preceded by a report stamping him as unreliable, lazy, and impervious to discipline. In short, if told in advance that their son was a liar and a miscreant, the Archduke Leopold Salvator and his wife would take Franz Josef's subsequent complaints with a substantial pinch of salt. Foremost in their consciousness would be the galling thought that he had merited a dishonorable discharge from Barcelona's most respected monastery school. It was not likely that they would want this disgraceful fact to become public.

El Tomate's reasoning was right. By the time Franz Josef reached the house in Sarriá, deep frowns furrowed the brows of his distressed parents. Had they not undergone enough mortification, first with Maria Antonia, then Assunta, and now this? Surely they had a right to expect some peace at last. . . .

Franz Josef tried to speak. He wanted to unburden his heart of all the stored grievances that he had not been able to write home about, but he found no sympathetic audience.

"Yes, yes," said Papa and Mama, cutting him short, "Soledad tried to tell us you were badly abused. But from the record of your conduct we can see that you gave ample provocation for whatever punishment you got. We are profoundly ashamed!"

It was an appalling dénouement.

Were all parents struck blind where the younger generation was concerned? Must children invariably be wrong? Perhaps here lay the secret of Bonanova's continued and flourishing success. Franz Josef had long wondered how the school could remain open, with pupils being graduated from it every year and stepping out into the world. Surely the truth must leak out and eventually be screamed from the housetops. Yet here were his own mother and father, doubting, and adding insult to injury with their accusation: "You must have got what you deserved——"

He was beside himself. If this were possible, how many wrongs must exist on earth, unrecognized, unaired, ignored because men wished to ignore them! What untold misery humanity must have endured to grow so callous against injustice!

Dimly a vision began to take shape in his mind. He

would align himself with the innocent, the disinherited, the oppressed, for whom there was no spokesman and no help. He had learned from bitter experience what it was to be the underdog and scapegoat, lashed by the whip of a bully. It was an insignificant schoolboy tragedy, but he would be marked by it for life.

Chapter Seventeen

EXPULSION WAS NOT an ideal way to finish school. Franz Josef would walk a thorny path before wiping this dark blot from his record.

"What do you propose to do?" asked his parents after dismissing the subject of Bonanova as too unpalatable for further discussion.

He had no ready answer to this question. For months the mere thought of coming home had filled his waking hours, until it had become a burning obsession. But he could see that the house in Sarriá would be no haven. His parents were embarrassed by the son who had brought them such disgrace.

"I want to be an aviator." He suddenly blurted out a long-cherished ambition.

The Infanta Blanca cast a shocked glance at her spouse. "There we have the result of Anton's example!" she said bitterly. "If all our boys become fliers we might as well buy them cemetery lots for Christmas, because they'll need them very soon!"

Papa belittled the matter. "I hardly think Pepi will pass entrance examinations to a secondary engineering school. He'll have to do a lot better than he has so far, to become even a garage mechanic."

The words stung, but Franz Josef swallowed them. Only recently his brother Anton had been graduated from the Areneros Institute in Madrid and had gone to England as a full-fledged electrical and mechanical engineer; he was now at Brooklands Airdrome near Croydon, learning to fly. But Anton's books were at home. He, Franz Josef, could

Marie Antoinette Brooch, engagement present from
Franz Josef to Marta.

Archduke Franz Josef's Castle "Hernstein," near Vienna.

study those books and make up for the fiasco of Bonanova. By cramming like mad, one could certainly pass entrance examinations anywhere.

"Very well," was the family verdict. Let him try and see. Anton's success was no measure; Anton had always been exceptionally gifted and quick to learn whatever he put his mind to. Had he not soloed over the Kentish Downs, four and a half hours after touching the controls of his first plane? Yes, here was something to shoot at. As a boy of twelve Anton had built his first radio receiving set with a raw potato, some nails, and a bit of twisted wire. No such feats had ever been reported about the Archduke Pepi.

But Pepi was not discouraged. He loved and admired Anton (perhaps above all his brothers and sisters) because of their proximity to each other in age and tastes. Nothing could be more inspiring than to chart one's course after such a model. Decidedly, Franz Josef thought he would have a try.

He began by studying at home and taking night courses at the University of Barcelona. In addition, as his allowance was small and his plans were ambitious, it became necessary to make a little money on the side. Papa had taunted him about not meeting the qualifications of a garage mechanic. Well, why not find out? He went off one afternoon and got himself a job: as a garage mechanic. Not yet eighteen, he became self-supporting.

The job, which took up every afternoon thenceforth, including holidays, opened up new horizons. A fellow worker named Pablo Riba repaired trucks and initiated Franz Josef into the primary task of taking apart a chassis and a gasoline motor. Nobody at the garage suspected that the new apprentice was an imperial prince. As his friendship with Pablo blossomed, Franz Josef found himself presently invited to the Riba home on the opposite side of town. Here he met Old Vicente Riba, Pablo's father.

Old Vicente had been a saddler in his youth and he had never lost the smell of leather. During the subsequent carriage era he had been forced to change trades, becoming a painter of wagons, hearses, and landaus. Then, with the arrival of the machine age, further degradation awaited him. He was today "reduced" to daubing automobiles, a task his artist soul despised.

For some inexplicable reason a great affinity sprang up between Old Vicente and Francisco, as the new handyman at the garage was called. Despite the vast gap of years between them they became even better friends than Franz Josef and Pablo had been. Perhaps a dilapidated secondhand motorcycle had something to do with it.

The Archduke had acquired the motorcycle for sixty pesetas at a scrap sale, and he hoped to put it back into working condition. Among other vital improvements the wretched vehicle needed a new gasoline tank, a set of tires, and a coat of paint. The last of these led to a business transaction with Old Vicente. Franz Josef came to the Riba shop to buy a can of paint.

"Bring your blasted wheelbarrow here," grumbled Vicente scornfully. "We'll do the job together."

Franz Josef eagerly accepted the offer, and the motorcycle was done up in a magnificent bullfighter red. It looked so handsome that Vicente went through the junk pile in his back yard and found an old discarded klaxon, which was prominently attached to the left handle bar. In its new dress the motorcycle garnered the plaudits of the entire neighborhood. There was only one thing wrong: it would not run. Even so, an entranced customer soon put in an appearance

and the contraption was sold for ninety pesetas, a fifty percent profit.

The Archduke promptly offered Vicente a share in payment for the klaxon, but the old man would not hear of it.

"If you pay me," he protested, "you might not come back
to see me. And I do enjoy your visits——"

It was not clear just what bound the rough and humble
Vicente to his unknown friend. Certainly the association
was not profitable: it cost the old man money, what with
not realizing a gain on his paint or counting hours of unpaid labor. Yet there was something about the youth to
which the peasant responded. Franz Josef had that courtli-
ness of the high-born which is so seldom seen in the high-
born. Even in overalls, with grease-spattered face and hands,
he had the deference and gentility given only to a story-book
prince.

"I will make you a proposition," said Vicente after their
first alleged business venture terminated. "My competitor,
Fermín Malaventura, owns a slightly damaged motorcycle
with a sidecar. And this marvelous object can be had for
exactly two hundred pesetas——"

The Archduke shook his head sadly. "I don't have two
hundred pesetas. It will take me forever to earn that much,
and I have to save for my tutoring at the university."

"*Qué diablos!*" Vicente protested. "You possess ninety already. The rest can be borrowed!"

"Borrowed? From whom?"

The old man slapped his trouser pocket. There was a
modest jingle.

"Oh, no," Franz Josef replied quickly, "you would not let
me pay back!"

At this the other looked up archly. "There is a way, Francisco, in which you can pay——"

"How?"

A wistful gleam came into Vicente's eye. "Never have I sat in a sidecar, *haciendo el señor* ('making the gentleman'). . . . If you will take me riding one day——"

"In the sidecar?"

"*Ay*—but yes—in the sidecar! My happiness will be complete!'

This left Franz Josef really no choice. The motorcycle of Fermín Malaventura was bought on the spot and carried—it, too, did not run—across the street to Vicente's shop. Almost two weeks were spent in taking it apart and coaxing its insides back into working order. There was also the obligatory paint job, since one's first ride in a sidecar must not be marred by dinginess or unseemly appearance. Vicente would make his debut in yellow and green lacquer. He wished to be seen—"making the gentleman"—from a great distance, and with a dramatic splash.

At last all was ready and the glad day arrived. "Where shall we go?" Franz Josef asked, as they had not given thought to an itinerary.

It was perhaps fitting that Vicente should choose an excursion to Monserrat, the mighty cliff sanctuary above Barcelona, which legend held to be the seat of the Holy Grail. A passable road led northwest of the city for thirty miles to the foot of the giant Sierra—named *Mons Serratus* in Roman times because of the sawlike, jagged piling of rock that cut its sharp profile against the sky.

"We can reach the Benedictine Monastery above the Valle Malo (Evil Vale) before noon," explained the excited old man. "The monks will bless medals for us and allow us to partake of their *garbanzo* soup, in return for which we bring them a supply of matches and votive candles." Due to mountain humidity these constituted a welcome gift.

Franz Josef felt himself transported into a world of unreality. He had been in Barcelona now for several years, yet no one had pointed out to him that above this industrialized Catalan city there rose the lofty retreat held sacred in the sagas of many peoples. The Arthurian Knights, the followers of Furnival, Chrétien de Troyes, Parsifal—all had given themselves over to the quest for holiness and salvation on the heights of a Never-Never Land which they called Monsalvat (*Mons Salvationis*). But it had been Spain's destiny to lend the ancient symbol its living form.

How did this come to pass?

At the time of the Crucifixion the great range of the Pyrenees had been shaken by violent earthquakes, manifesting to the Caesars that no corner of their empire remained untouched by the immolation of the Son of Man. Shortly thereafter Saint Peter crossed the Mediterranean, bearing an image of the Virgin (fashioned by the Apostle Luke) to guard the terrible crevasses of Valle Malo and save Catalan travelers from harm. Legend also added that the Grail or hallowed goblet from which Christ drank at the Last Supper found its way to the Spanish shrine, though there were those who said the Grail was actually the vessel in which Joseph of Arimathea caught the blood from the wound in the Lord's side. The strange occidental name of Grail, Gral, or Grazal, was Provençal for bowl or drinking cup.

Vicente had no erudite ideas concerning Monserrat. But he did know the story behind the Two Madonnas. There was the original Virgin of Saint Luke, which had been lost during the Moorish invasion of 717 A.D., and was later replaced by a second image carved of darkest ebony. The latter became officially known as *Nuestra Señora de Monserrat y Santísima Patrona de Cataluña,* though devotees referred to her simply as *La Patrona*. Despite her dusky complexion, the Black Madonna was highly venerated and visited by thousands of pilgrims annually from every province in Spain, for she was deemed extraordinarily miraculous. But she also had her troubles. For, in the year 880, long after the expulsion of the Moors, Bishop Gondemar of Vich had walked over the rocky pinnacles and spires toward the summit known as Turó (Tower) de San Gerónimo, four thousand feet above the sea. From the lookout of La Miranda he had gazed at the barren chalk formations, cloven by ravines and precipices, as far down as the River Llobregat which circled Barcelona to the southwest. It was now that the good prelate was startled from his reverie by the sound of soft music and the wafting of sweet smells. Turning about, he saw the image of the lost Madonna of Saint Luke, reposing in a cave. There was nothing for it but to bear the tidings back to town and to promote the erection of a church in her honor.

At this point the followers of *La Patrona* took umbrage. Would the recovery of the earlier image deflect the faithful from the Black Madonna's shrine? The matter very nearly led to a holy war until, by edict from the Vatican, it was decreed that both Virgins were equally venerable and to be accorded the same honors. Even so, a secret rivalry persisted into modern times. The followers of both Saint Luke's image and *La Patrona* outdid one another in supplying their respective oratories with untold treasures, while the Heavenly Ladies themselves seemed to be engaged in a tournament for the title of the best robed and most bejeweled.

Like most Catalans of humble station, Vicente's loyalty belonged to *La·Patrona*.

"She cured me of the ague," he said, "and blessed my

brother's wife with two sets of twins." In all, a generous show of favoritism.

What captured Franz Josef's imagination was not the actual existence of a place called Monserrat, but the mystic power of its legend. Was not the Holy Grail in itself an embodiment of the Unattainable, in the mere search of which the soul grew strengthened and purified? The blessing then lay in the pilgrimage, spiritual rather than physical, made toward the ideal that man set for himself.

> *"Die Gralsburg liegt*
> *im Sehnsuchtsland!"*
> ("The Castle of the Grail
> lies in the Land of Longing!")

Vicente was most certainly en route there. For he sat in the yellow and green motorcycle sidecar, *haciendo el señor,* and smoking an impressive black cigar. The cigar was a cheap *caliqueño,* noteworthy for its stench and poor burning quality. To keep it aglow required an incredible number of matches.

By the time the two happy pilgrims reached the heights of Monserrat the gift intended for the Benedictine Fathers had dwindled. The matches were gone. There was nothing left but the packet of votive candles.

Chapter Eighteen

DESCENDING, Vicente proposed a detour through the town of Vich, made famous by that same Bishop Gondemar who had recovered the lost Madonna of Saint Luke. At Vich, Vicente had a brother, Fidencio, who was a baker.

"Fidencio's son is getting married this week," he remembered cheerfully. "We might be just in time for the wedding!"

The suggestion proved opportune. As the ill-matched travelers drew up before the bakery shop the strains of *gitano* music greeted their ears, while the aroma of savory roast pig gave evidence that a celebration was in full swing. Someone had toasted the bride and groom:

"Salud y pesetas!" ("Health and wealth!")

To which the assembled guests responded with the traditional *"Y tiempo para gastarlas!"* ("And time to squander them!")

As for Fidencio and Vicente, though they lived only some twenty miles apart, they saluted each other with the effusion of long-lost kinsmen. From their tears and embraces one might have judged that the brothers had been separated by an ocean and two continents since youth. For a moment the wedding feast assumed a secondary importance while the two oldsters enjoyed a bibulous reunion.

Franz Josef found the proceedings altogether novel. He had been introduced as a garage hand from Barcelona, which gave him at once a certain prestige. Was not the bridegroom, like Vicente's son Pablo, a truck driver?

But what fascinated the Archduke in particular was his first glimpse of the interior of a village bakery. Fiden-

cio's place was small and it had been turned topsy-turvy for
the fiesta. A long table had been improvised by means of
boards laid across flour barrels, while boxes and crates sup-
plemented the scant number of benches and chairs. The
bridal pair naturally enjoyed the spotlight on a dais sur-
mounted by the front seat of Papa Fidencio's delivery *tar-
tana* (two-wheeled donkey cart).

The party broke up before midnight, since most of those
present were workers who must rise early the next morning.
Fidencio himself started his baking at four o'clock.

"We'll all get up and help," said Vicente reassuringly as
Fidencio's wife began to clear a space before the brick oven.
"Just go to bed and catch some sleep!"

This was more easily said than done, for, with the bride
and the new in-laws on the premises, there were not enough
cots to go around. In the end the older folks doubled up on
spare mattresses spread across the floor of the dough room,
while the bridal pair made use of the front chamber with its
great four-poster bed. Franz Josef shared a *catre* (canvas
cot) with Vicente and Manolín, a younger brother of the
groom.

Early the next morning the Archduke was awakened by
the pungent smoke of pine twigs crackling in the oven. Fidencio and his wife were already kneading the dough, while
other members of the household dusted the baking tins and
pans. It was still dark and a hush lay over these labors as
though they might be some primitive religious rite. From
time immemorial the making of bread seemed to be linked
with hallowed rituals, threatened only where modern machines encroached upon the ancient manual chore. Fidencio's bakery was operated along patriarchal lines: once the
loaves emerged crisp and brown from the hot oven, Manolín
and two assistants made the delivery rounds, while Papa

Fidencio and his wife attended matins at the near-by church. On special occasions, like today, the whole household went to the cathedral, lately renowned because of the new murals by José María Sert.

Returning at last to Barcelona, after a week end crowded with unforgettable impressions, Franz Josef attacked his studies with renewed vigor. The inspiring beauty of Monserrat no less than the homely scenes he had witnessed at Vich filled his heart with a warm zest for life. He longed to work and to achieve a goal that might assure him the satisfaction and dignity known by Fidencio, the baker.

Old Vicente too came back refreshed. Indeed, the ride in the sidecar seemed to have rejuvenated him, for he suddenly hit upon a bold idea. Why not sell the second motorcycle at a fancy price, on account of its passenger accommodation, and buy an automobile? He, Vicente, had never sat in an automobile. . . .

Franz Josef was aghast. Did the poor fellow know what he was talking about? Even the most dilapidated Ford or secondhand Citroën cost a fortune far beyond the price a remodeled motorcycle could bring.

"In spite of the paint job?" Vicente asked, eying his handiwork with pride.

"Yes," Franz Josef disillusioned him. "It has something to do with cylinders and spark plugs, rather than a pleasing color scheme."

The old man brooded dejectedly, though not for long. Fumbling through his broad gaucho belt, which was fastened with four thongs and buckles, to hold in his stomach like a corselet, he pulled out a leather pouch. It contained the savings of a lifetime.

"Here," he said, "I want to make you another loan."

"But that's absurd! And in any case, it probably wouldn't be enough——"

Now Vicente was offended. "Not enough? Nearly five hundred pesetas, and he says it is not enough!"

"I didn't mean it that way, *amigo*. Five hundred pesetas is a fortune. I have never possessed so much money myself. But it won't buy a car——"

"A very broken-down car it *will* buy," Vicente persisted confidently. "Then we go to work with the repairs and the paint until, by the saints, she is a beauty. We take another ride to Monserrat and visit *La Patrona*——"

"And after that?"

"We sell the car for double the investment. We have a fortune and I will let you pay your debts, yes?"

It was an irresistible offer that could not be refused. Franz Josef accepted on condition that Vicente and his son Pablo pick out the "very broken-down" wreck on which they would try out their magic. Father and son readily agreed to this. From a near-by junk yard they salvaged a disreputable Fiat phaeton. It lacked bumpers, headlights, and a brake, but the price was happily within their budget. With Pablo at the steering wheel, Vicente and the Archduke pushed the decrepit vehicle uphill to the saddler's shop.

They went to work on it at once, ripping out parts and setting them together again. Through Pablo a fine brake was obtained from an American truck, as well as a pair of headlights and a bright radiator cap. For a color scheme Vicente chose a vivid blue, as luminous as his own hopes.

The job was finished in a fraction over two weeks and the result, optically at least, rewarded the industrious friends for their labors. Up and down the street people came to marvel.

"Es un coche estupendo!" they exclaimed, throwing up

their hands in admiration. The pile of junk had indeed been converted into a state coach.

Vicente glowed with anticipation and pride. If the earlier expedition by motorcycle had been a source of satisfaction, the forthcoming trip to Monserrat would amount to a triumphal progress. To think that in his old age he, Vicente, was to ride—*haciendo el señor*—in his own automobile!

The journey was planned for the following Sunday, and this time, allowing for Vicente's cigar, an extra large pack of matches was taken along to make certain that the monks would not again be cheated of their supply.

A little crowd of spectators gathered before the saddler's shop on the morning of departure. Franz Josef took the wheel, while beside him—puffing at his *caliqueño*—sat Vicente in Catalan dress, broad belt, and beret. Pablo stood in the street, crank in hand, as the *coche estupendo* had no starter. The great moment had come.

"*Listo!*" cried Old Vicente, waving to his son. "Ready!"

Pablo stooped over and began to crank. His face grew red, then purple, yet no sound issued from the motor beyond a faint sputtering gasp.

"*Listo!*" the crowd chorused, lending support to Pablo's efforts. And now, suddenly, the ignition caught on. There was a sharp puff, followed by a shattering explosion. Behind a column of smoke and flame which burst from the clattering hood, the car collapsed in the street. Unhurt, but shaken, the Archduke and his passenger leaped to safety.

A bucket brigade was quickly formed, bearing water from the house and putting out the blaze. What remained of the proud chariot was a sorry spectacle.

"What shall we do now?" asked Franz Josef, bedraggled and almost in tears.

Vicente fell back upon his indestructible peasant dignity.

"*Primero vamos a tomar almuerzo,*" he commanded. "First, let us have lunch!"

Unruffled, he led the way into the house where his wife and the womenfolk of the neighborhood set food upon the table. A solid repast was consumed, with red wine and sturdy corn bread, before Vicente would consent to look again upon the catastrophe outside his door. Only when he had eaten and composed himself did he lend a hand in clearing up the litter.

"We'll put it together again," he mumbled· stubbornly into his beard. "You wait and see——"

Actually, Franz Josef, Pablo, and the old man went to work again on the derelict remains, soldering and patching each fragment of the chassis, and smoothing every length of tangled coil. Four months went by at this arduous task, but at the end of that time the car stood once more on four wheels.

During this period Old Vicente underwent a spiritual regeneration.

"I don't think *La Patrona* wants me to visit her in pomp and comfort," he reflected, canceling the projected excursion to the Black Madonna of Monserrat. "She does not like automobiles!"

As for his life savings, Fate dealt kindly with Vicente. With the aid of Pablo and Franz Josef the rebuilt car was pushed (no one dared start the motor again) to the opposite end of town where it was sold at auction. It brought the handsome price of eight hundred pesetas—a sixty-percent profit.

Upon this happy climax the partnership was dissolved, as the Archduke was ready to take his entrance examinations for the Escuela Industrial and would thenceforth be unable to continue at his garage job.

Vicente for his part promised to undertake the pilgrimage to Monserrat in Franz Josef's absence, as soon as the weather cleared and mountain paths were safe for hiking.

"They who seek the Grail," mused Old Vicente, "must go on foot. . . ."

Chapter Nineteen

THE POLITICAL SITUATION in Spain was at this time a precarious one. While Alfonso XIII had succeeded in walking the tight wire of neutrality throughout the European conflict of 1914-1918, Spain had become embroiled in colonial difficulties. Across the Strait of Gibraltar, in Morocco, the Riff leader Abd-el-Krim had incited his tribesmen to rebellion against domination from Madrid.

It was a minor uprising that could have been put down with a single well-equipped and efficiently directed military expedition. But both Alfonso and his government took the matter lightly, dispatching only a few conscripts to Africa where, it was assumed, their mere arrival would quell native resistance.

The error proved costly. Abd-el-Krim slaughtered the vanguard of bewildered Spaniards and entrenched himself to await the second batch, which was not long in coming. Still unaware of the enemy's stature, Madrid sent out another trickle of ill-prepared militia without tanks or heavy artillery, only to meet with a second drubbing at the hands of the fierce desert tribes.

Grumbling began to be heard throughout Spain as casualty lists poured homeward from the African front. Parents and widows of fallen soldiers railed against the desultory conduct of the war. The King, it was observed, continued his gay sporting life at the famed spas of Santander and San Sebastián, while theaters and cafés were crowded with dashing officers, seemingly on perpetual leave. Was the fight against Abd-el-Krim for the poor man only?

Must conscripts die on foreign soil in order to safeguard the night life of their gold-braided superiors?

As new recruiting drives were launched in Catalonia and the Basque Provinces, the populace rose in angry demonstrations, not only against the unpopular colonial campaign but against centralized authority as represented by the King. The old spark of Catalan and Basque nationalism was ignited again and fanned to a quick flame. At Barcelona separatist patriots argued for immediate establishment of democratic home rule. They formed a delegation which was to appear before the Cortes in Madrid for a defiant presentation of the Catalan case.

Alfonso XIII at last took notice. Turning from racing forms, lady loves and bullfights, he gave some thought to the jeopardy that faced his kingdom. Something must be done, and it must be done fast. One single striking success in Africa might save the day. But who could win him this success?

After some reflection the monarch singled out a brusque, daring cavalry officer, General Silvestre, for the task. Silvestre was to set out with a special expeditionary army on a nonstop march into the Riff, from Melilla straight to Alhucemas, a distance of approximately forty miles. By this strategic move the forces of Abd-el-Krim could be bottled up and driven into the sea, bringing the war to a triumphant conclusion.

To lend further weight to his plan, Alfonso timed the new campaign to coincide with the holiday of Saint James Matamoros (Killer-of-Moors), the ancient patron of Spain. On this day the King was scheduled to make a speech during the solemn removal of the remains of *El Cid* to Burgos Cathedral. It was an occasion for piety and patriotic pride, ideally suited for the quelling of incipient discontent.

Despite these calculations, something went wrong with the well-planned offensive of General Silvestre. On June 23, 1921, the Spanish columns found themselves suddenly ambushed by Riff tribesmen issuing from the abandoned fortress of Anual. Ten thousand of Silvestre's men were killed, four thousand taken prisoner, while rifles, cannon, machine guns, and a score of airplanes were seized as booty. The General himself, on the point of capture, committed suicide. Nor did the debacle end there. A fortnight later the Spanish garrison of Monte Arruit was compelled to surrender; the troops, numbering seven thousand, were massacred in cold blood, while the commanding officer and his staff were carried off in chains and held for ransom. Melilla, the proud city from which Silvestre was to have started his victorious march, now trembled under siege.

Alfonso did not make a very good speech at Burgos Cathedral. Instead he hurried back to Madrid, where a commission of inquiry was already investigating the military disaster. Unpleasant truths were aired. The Silvestre expedition, like those that had preceded it, evidently had been undertaken in the spirit of a lark. On the day of the battle at Anual many leading officers had left their units to attend the opening of a cabaret and a resort hotel in Melilla; others had remained behind in Málaga, happily drugged with wine. In addition, there was the usual Latin confusion and indiscipline, particularly amid air-force personnel. Pilots left their planes unguarded while they slept in comfortable billets located in distant towns. In the face of such laxity the enemy had made short shrift of Alfonso's braves. In a public statement Abd-el-Krim himself admitted that victory had been made easy for him through Spanish inefficiency.

But the Madrid inquiry brought out something else which proved incriminating to the King. A letter had been found among General Silvestre's effects, in which Alfonso revealed that the fatal campaign had been undertaken against the advice of Parliament.

"*Haga lo que yo le digo,*" wrote His Majesty, "*sin hacer caso al Ministro de Guerra, quien es un imbécil . . .*" ("Do as I tell you, without paying attention to the Minister of War, who is an imbecile . . .")

In publishing its findings the committee would place full responsibility upon the King's shoulders, not only for the disaster in Africa, but for the heavy taxation imposed by the unwanted colonial war. The report was to be read aloud at the first autumn meeting of the Cortes and then given to the newspapers. This exposure would be almost certain to cost Alfonso his throne.

It was in sheer desperation that the King now took an extraordinary step. On September 13, 1923, he summoned the Captain-General of Catalonia, Miguel Primo de Rivera, to disband the Cortes and set up a military dictatorship. By this stroke the embarrassing disclosures were hushed up and a public scandal was averted. True, with a dictator in control, Alfonso voluntarily resigned himself to playing second fiddle, a situation highly distasteful to him. But it was the only way to save the crown.

Under Primo de Rivera the Moroccan War was to drag on for another six years at a cost of several billion pesetas and an untold sacrifice of lives. Nor did Spain, at the conclusion of hostilities in 1929, carry off the palm of victory. For it was France that brought the Riffians to their knees. In one of his advances, Abd-el-Krim had mistakenly crossed into French Morocco and engaged Zouave defenders in combat. A declaration of war followed, furnishing Spain with an unexpected ally.

From now on the fighting gained momentum as the

French threw their expertly trained colonials into the fray. Within a matter of weeks Abd-el-Krim's capital, Axdir, was occupied and the great Arab leader taken prisoner. Thus Spain's long tradition of failure on African soil was redeemed by a spurt of neighborly assistance.

After the fashion of dictators, Primo de Rivera took full credit for the final termination of the Riffian struggle. As the French disappeared once more across the border and retired to their garrisons at Fez, Primo donned a laurel wreath and rode in state through the streets of Madrid. This was too much even for the King, whom the Dictator had been hired to protect. With Morocco pacified at last, Alfonso decided to get rid of the pompous Rivera.

It was not difficult to find a pretext for toppling the unpopular Dictator from his eminence. Rivera had governed as a reactionary, indifferent to Spain's crying need for social and agrarian reform. To set the populace against him it was merely necessary to set up a rival candidate who promised to heed the nation's most urgent demands. Alfonso picked his man in the person of another general, named Damaso Berenguer. Following a *coup d'état,* identical to the one which had brought him into power, Rivera was packed off to Paris, where he ended his days in disillusion and bitterness.

As for Berenguer, Alfonso did not find in him the solution to his problems. Anti-monarchist feeling was on the increase in every corner of the land, leading to riots and demonstrations which no substitute dictator could quell. Rivera's usefulness had ended with the Moroccan campaign; for Berenguer there was no excuse. The question that now occupied the country at large was whether there could be any further excuse for the King.

Unable to set up a second dictatorship, Alfonso tried various expedients for re-establishing the Cortes and normal constitutional government, without risk of a general election which might strip him of all power. But he could not obtain the necessary promises of support from either the Liberal middle classes, Labor, or the outstanding political leaders. At last, after infinite hesitations, he agreed to allow municipal elections and to gamble on a surge of pro-monarchist votes.

He was due for a shattering disappointment. All but four provinces in Spain out of fifty went Republican, with Madrid and Barcelona leading the avalanche. The King had been deserted by so overwhelming a majority that the Army and the Civil Guard, commanded by General Sanjurjo, withdrew their support, while even the Grandees held aloof for fear of Communist uprisings that imperiled their own position. In short, by his own royalist clique Alfonso was urged to abdicate.

Sadly the sovereign with the Habsburg blood and Bourbon profile packed his bags. There was not much to take along, since the trappings of royalty were useless in exile. As Grand Master of eight Spanish orders of knighthood he possessed a wardrobe of gala costumes and decorations, which henceforth would give way to simple mufti. It pained him particularly not to wear again his prized *Toisón de Oro* (Golden Fleece) with its linked escutcheons of Castile, León, Granada, plus the lilies of Bourbon, the double eagle of Austria, and the arms of Savoy, Sicily, and Brabant.

No indignity attached itself to the King's departure. As a human being Alfonso had been considered *simpático* and was well liked; hence Spain accorded him the gesture of a gallant farewell. He traveled on a battleship with full escort and a one-hundred-gun salute.

Thereafter the royal standard bearing the once illustrious *Torres y Leones* (Turrets and Lions) of Spain was lowered over the Palace of El Pardo in Madrid. It would not be hoisted to flutter in the breeze above the obscure Fontainebleau hotel whither Queen Ena followed her husband into exile.

Chapter Twenty

THE SHIFT FROM MONARCHY to republic affected the lives of all who had close contact with Spain's royal house.

At Lequeitio on the Basque coast, where the Empress Zita and her children had lately found refuge, trunks were hastily packed before the gathering storm. If Alfonso toppled from power there was no security for Zita who, everyone knew, dreamed only of restoration (for herself or her son Otto) to Hungary's throne. It was not that Spaniards lacked gallantry or wished to show themselves inhospitable toward the widowed refugee. But Zita had aspirations. She embodied the very essence of dynastic irredentism, able to renounce everything—luxury, comfort, happiness—except the regal purple. For such a guest the new republic of Niceto Alcalá Zamora could have no place.

Of course she was not driven out of Spain. At her own leisure the Empress made plans for removal to France, and later Belgium, where the Prince of Croix placed his château of Steenockerzeel at her disposal.

What fate awaited the Barcelona Habsburgs? At Sarriá the Archduke Leopold Salvator pondered his lot and that of his large family. Were they to be uprooted again and set adrift in an increasingly unfriendly world? The problem had grave financial aspects inasmuch as the cash obtained from Papa's French patents had gone into Spanish real estate and the establishment of a supposedly permanent home. If they must move again it would be necessary to dig up some money.

As early as the Rivera dictatorship, when Alfonso's kingly

might was first threatened, the Infanta Blanca had discerned the ominous handwriting on the wall.

"There is bad weather ahead," she had said significantly. "I think we had better provide ourselves with a substantial umbrella."

Heretofore, in time of need, she had summoned the Parisian jeweler Romoeuf for appraisal and purchase of another emerald from her prized necklace. A single stone had managed to tide them over many a critical impasse. But Leopold Salvator objected to this practice. The necklace had been his own wedding present to his bride; he could not watch its gradual dissolution without a profound sense of humiliation.

"I have a better idea," he announced as the Infanta prepared to send for Romoeuf. "The Diadem of Hortense is still in Vienna, with Stepanek. Perhaps it can be sold."

It was a capital suggestion. With the present unfavorable outlook it did not seem likely that the Infanta Blanca would have occasion to don the historic tiara. For all practical purposes the Diadem of Hortense was of less value to her than a pair of stout walking shoes. Yes, there must be a way to put the useless trinket on the market.

Opportunity smiled in the person of a former Austrian officer of Polish origin, Captain Josef von Korvin, who chanced to be passing through Barcelona en route to Vienna. Korvin had served in the Austrian Artillery under Archduke Leopold Salvator during the war, and it was natural that he should call on his former commander. But there were other bonds that tied him to the archducal family. These were of an unmilitary nature.

Years ago, during his heyday as an inventor, Papa had also developed an interest in aeronautics. He had purchased a balloon, manufactured in Austria and proudly named *Meteor*, with which to navigate across Europe.

After some experimental ascents at home a cross-Channel
flight became his goal. Due to prevailing winds, blowing
landward from the west, it was decided to make the attempt
from England to France, rather than vice versa. The balloon was folded up and stuffed into its own gondola, to be
shipped as freight to London where Papa, with the assistance
of Captain Korvin, meant to reassemble it and launch upon
the first Channel crossing by air.

At the last moment the Archduke Leopold Salvator found
himself restrained by official duties, whereupon his brother-
in-law Don Jaime offered to make the trip. The dapper
Spanish Pretender, something of a dandy in his goatee and
beret, had long yearned to take to the air and experience
man's latest technical adventure. With Korvin and the
crated *Meteor* he set out for England.

In London the visitors were well received. Indeed, Don
Jaime was lionized by fashionable hostesses who emitted
flattering gasps at his courage and enterprise. Nightly the
pair attended elegant receptions where they held forth on
the morrow's plans, namely the testing of aerial currents
and checking of weather charts so as to start on their epoch-
making flight. But British climate was against them. At
dawn each day Korvin unpacked the *Meteor* in a meadow
near Ascot and pumped it partially full of gas, only to give
up in despair. The heavy atmosphere and becalmed winds
paralyzed every attempt.

This state of affairs dragged on for weeks, throwing a
pall upon even the most fluttering hostesses. From drawing
rooms and banquet halls Don Jaime turned for variety to the
capital's music halls and restaurants. Marking time until a
favorable turn in the weather, he explored the sights of
Soho, where an awkward experience befell him. While sip-
ping ale in a cozy barroom corner with Korvin at his side,

the Pretender was accosted by a dancing girl who gaily pulled a chair up to the table. More drinks were ordered and in the conviviality that ensued the young lady edged more closely toward the foreign guests until Don Jaime felt a suspicious tug at his pocket. Reaching for his wallet he discovered that his cash—some forty pounds—had disappeared. But at the same time he observed that the pretty and very entertaining "hostess" was busying herself with a pottery vase containing some artificial flowers. Realizing that the container held no water, he remained unruffled and continued to enjoy the merry evening until, at the moment of departing, he quietly reached into the vase and retrieved his money.

On returning to his hotel that evening, Don Jaime emptied his effects on the night table and discovered to his amazement that his cash had swelled to several hundred pounds, a sum he definitely did not recall carrying in his pocket. The barroom lass had evidently done a bit of collecting through the evening, with Don Jaime ending as the unwitting beneficiary. Abashed at his ill-gotten gains, doubly ill-gotten if the dancing girl had in the same manner rooked other customers, His Royal Highness tossed sleeplessly in bed. There was only one thing to do. At breakfast the Pretender decided to send Korvin off alone to study the prevailing zephyrs, while he himself tried to make contact with the pilfering wench whose name he remembered as Gertie.

In Soho, it developed, Gertie was well known but inaccessible in daytime as she 'ad to 'ave 'er sleep. Diffidently Don Jaime explained to the barroom owner that there must have been a few drinks too many the night before, as he was suffering deplorable aftereffects; in short, he needed one more hair off the dog that bit him. The barman had no objection. A moment later His Royal Highness sat at the same table with the pottery vase before him, and a tankard of foaming stout coming up. It was an easy matter, between sips, to replace Gertie's hoard in the innocent-looking receptacle and to saunter out with a reasonably refreshed conscience. Whether, in not turning the girl over to the police, Don Jaime became an accessory to her misdeeds remained a moot question. He preferred not to probe more deeply into the matter.

Korvin meanwhile had run into a chain of circumstances that climaxed in a sensational crisis. On the one morning when his royal companion had refused to come to the field for meteorological tests and investigations, the beastly weather took a sudden turn. The fog lifted, a smiling sky extended overhead, and a fine breeze whipped in from the west. In short, while rising on a trial flight Korvin found himself swept up on an invigorating gale and blown out toward the Channel.

After the first shock he had waved to his ground crew and tossed out emergency ropes, but he was beyond reach in a rudderless craft, for the *Meteor* was a "free" rather than a "captive" balloon. Furthermore, sighting water below him in almost no time, Korvin preferred not to deflate and make a forced descent as he carried no seagoing equipment beyond a dubious lifebelt. There would be little point in bobbing alone for hours or days in a briny bath, miles off the scant shipping lanes that traced the Channel in those times. He had really no choice except to whizz briskly toward France without Don Jaime aboard.

The crossing went off well enough. Before long the intrepid balloonist sighted Arras, between Amiens and Lille in the Department of Pas-de-Calais. But suddenly, from inland, a squall arose and seized the helpless craft, blowing it out to

sea once more. In addition the gas bag leaked gradually
and was losing altitude, threatening to drop into the foamy
depths. Alarmed, Korvin threw ballast overboard, including
sandbags, compass, binoculars, watch, shoes, coat and pants.
Relieved of everything but his drawers, the young man was
now wafted shoreward again toward Arras, where he managed to descend neatly upon a sixteenth-century belfry in the
Petite Place. The exploit earned him encomiums throughout Europe, as well as the gratitude of the balloon's owner,
Archduke Leopold Salvator. In a small way Austria had
taken a pioneering step in aviation.

It was the same Captain Korvin who now, almost two
decades later, became familiarized with the background of
the Hortense Diadem, which his exiled commander hoped
to turn into coin. After the jeweled ornament had been
given by Napoleon I to his stepdaughter Hortense, it had
reverted to his second wife Marie Louise; through the latter's son, the Duke of Reichstadt, it had finally reached
Vienna and become part of the Leopold Salvator family
treasure. Did Korvin care to attempt the sale? If so, he
would receive a handsome commission.

Essentially here was another flight in a trial balloon. The
former officer, now jobless and down on his luck, leaped at
the offer. He assured the Infanta Blanca of his eagerness to
serve the sister of his London travel-mate, Don Jaime. But
he must have credentials and a letter of introduction to
Stepanek in Vienna, so as to encounter no distrust. Also, a
small advance on expenses would be welcome.

With characteristic optimism the Archduke Leopold Salvator and his wife filled the above prerequisites and sent the
efficient Korvin on his way.

Six weeks went by without news. But as in the days—so
long ago—of the balloon flight, they were not worried. Com-

munications, one must remember, had been disrupted by postwar chaos. Besides, Korvin's mission was highly confidential in character, calling for the utmost discretion. Careless correspondence might jeopardize the whole undertaking.

The weeks dragged into months and still there was no word. Had something gone wrong? Ought one to send a telegram to Stepanek? But how should such a message be worded so as not to get the former tutor into trouble? The diadem, though private family property, might after all have been confiscated by the state, in which case any attempt at its recovery became an act of treason. In short, the hopeful venture seemed to have ended in a stalemate.

After six months had passed, the mystery was cleared through a freak accident reported in a Swiss paper. It concerned the crash of a truck of contraband on an Alpine pass above St. Gotthardt, in which a smuggler named Daniele lost his life. The incident did not at first appear to have any connection with the imperial jewel, as no other victim or survivor was found on the scene, and the damaged truck was one of a convoy carrying wood pulp and a concealed cargo of undeclared tobacco. Further investigation, however, disclosed shipping orders on which appeared the signature of Korvin. At this point the authorities of Switzerland and Austria plunged into a maze of research which ultimately uncovered a plot fit for a Nick Carter dime mystery.

Korvin, it appeared, had managed to reach Vienna and, with the aid of the archducal letters, to make contact with Stepanek. The latter had felt an instant distrust of his unknown guest, though he could not deny the authenticity of the signatures presented by Korvin. Reluctantly Stepanek handed over the tiara.

It would have been a simple matter now for Korvin to

conceal the treasure in a loaf of bread or some other disguise and to hasten back to Spain. But he had other ideas. Why not engage in a little profiteering on the side, before termination of the archducal mission? For example, one could pawn the diadem and buy some easily disposable merchandise, which in turn could be sold with an attractive margin of gain. After skimming off the profits, the gem would be recovered and handed to its rightful owners, with no one the wiser for what had transpired in the interim.

The more Korvin thought about it the better he liked his scheme. Besides, his good friend Daniele (who was experienced in such matters) thought it positively brilliant. Daniele knew a few elaborations of his own, however, which he did not mention to Korvin.

Combining their talents the two cronies set to work. They carried the diadem to Vienna's famous Dorotheum (State Pawn Shop) and received for it half a million pre-inflation kronen. With this sum they purchased a great quantity of export goods such as newsprint, paper, pulp, office equipment and other articles in demand on foreign markets. To make sure that the railroads did not take too large a cut they also obtained a fleet of discarded army trucks, which could later be dumped in Spain and Switzerland at a good price. In short, Korvin was by way of executing a master stroke. He was making use of, yet not actually abusing, his trust.

It proved to be Daniele, a congenital swindler, who upset the applecart or, in this case, the fleet of trucks. For Daniele had meant to carry out a private transaction in which Korvin was to have no part. Tucked away amid Korvin's legally declared wares Daniele had hidden a vast load of costly tobacco from Macedonia, which in Western Europe fetched high fees. To safeguard this valuable cargo the wily smuggler insisted on personally driving the first truck, with hired chauffeurs following closely behind him, and Korvin bringing up the rear.

What caused the accident could never be ascertained, though it appeared likely that Daniele was unfamiliar with mountain terrain. At a sharp curve the leading truck swerved off the road and went hurtling down into the abyss, taking the driver with it.

From the near-by Italian border a troop of *Carabinieri* joined Swiss mountain police in an attempted rescue. At sight of the contraband which had been spilled to right and left of the overturned vehicle, their attention fixed upon the remaining convoy, edging precariously along the overhanging cliffs. From here Korvin and his companions likewise surveyed the scene and realized that something was wrong. Without waiting to find out details, they detached a trailer from one of the truck cabs and made their escape.

As yet no visible link existed between the smuggling venture and the Hortense Diadem. But on reading an account in a Vienna newspaper the director of the Dorotheum recalled that two men named Korvin and Daniele had signed one of his pawn tickets. He reported this fact to the police, explaining that the transaction had involved a jewel of great worth.

Detectives hastened to the Dorotheum for an examination of the pawned article, only to find that it had been sold to an Amsterdam diamond broker who, when finally tracked down, admitted melting the "old-fashioned" setting and tossing the stones on the international gem mart. Here they had been seized upon by bidders from all over the world.

In short, the Diadem of Hortense had ceased to exist.

Coincidental with this blow the Archduke Leopold Salvator and his wife faced a second and no less poignant disap-

pointment. At the time of the family's flight from Vienna
the Infanta Blanca had entrusted a former co-worker in her
Red Cross unit with the keys to Castle Wilhelminenberg.
The person in question was a respectable matron named
Clara Jellinek whose husband held a post in the new
Austrian republic. Frau Jellinek, so the Infanta hoped, might
thus be able to salvage some castle furnishings before the
entire property had been confiscated.

The arrangement was as follows: all pieces of fine cabinet
work and historic value were to be put in storage, while
upholstered furniture (containing no rare wood) was to be
sold at auction. The proceeds of the latter would cover the
storage expenses and Frau Jellinek's commission.

Several years had gone by before the Barcelona Habsburgs ventured to inquire by letter about their abandoned
properties. Imperial estates and crown lands, everybody
knew, had been seized by decrees of expropriation. Castle
Wilhelminenberg, privately owned by the Archduke Leopold Salvator, was assessed by the new Republic at so high a
figure that the tax became exorbitant. As Papa was not able
to pay, the whole Galitzin Hill went on the block and was
bought by the City of Vienna, out of taxpayers' money. It
amounted to expropriation in a different form, since no other
bidders had presented themselves and the price was conse-
quently nominal. With deduction of new taxes accrued
during the family's absence in exile, the sum finally received
by Leopold Salvator amounted to a pittance.

But what had happened to rugs, pictures, table linens, cut-
lery, and other personal belongings? Indeed, what had
happened to Frau Jellinek?

No answer came to Papa's inquiry until he turned again
to the faithful tutor Stepanek, who soon uncovered an extraordinary story.

According to agreement the Jellineks, husband and wife, had emptied Castle Wilhelminenberg before its purchase by city funds. But they had misinterpreted further instructions in a manner suspiciously to their own advantage. For all valuable woods ended up at the Jellinek apartment—and in the households of two married Jellinek daughters—while the comparatively worthless overstuffed pieces had been put in storage. What was worse, the storage fees had remained unpaid, adding up to an impressive total.

There was no way of prosecuting the rascally Jellineks, any more than one could dodge payment of the storage bill. Only the lesson in exploitation and betrayal of confidence was free.

As for the earlier loss of the Hortense Diadem, a brief epilogue must be recorded. Seventeen years after his spectacular escape across the Alps, Korvin was caught and brought to justice on a charge of embezzlement. But by that time the Archduke Leopold Salvator derived little satisfaction from the news. He had died on September 4, 1931, long before the trial, at the age of sixty-eight.

¿Quiere usted admirar el panorama incomparable que ofrece Barcelona a vista de pájaro, volando sobre la ciudad?

¿Prefiere, simplemente, hacer un vuelo por los pintorescos alrededores del aeródromo?

¿Precisa usted trasladarse rápidamente, por vía aérea, a cualquier punto?

¿Le interesa aprender a conducir un avión, hacer fotografías aéreas, organizar algún festival aeronaútico?

CONSÚLTENOS SIEMPRE

Antonio y Francisco-José Habsburgo Borbón
AERÓDROMO "PRAT" (AEROPUERTO)

AGENCIA EN BARCELONA
COMPAÑÍA ESPAÑOLA DE TURISMO
PLAZA CATALUÑA, 1 - TELÉFONO 15338

The "Flying Archdukes" offer their services.

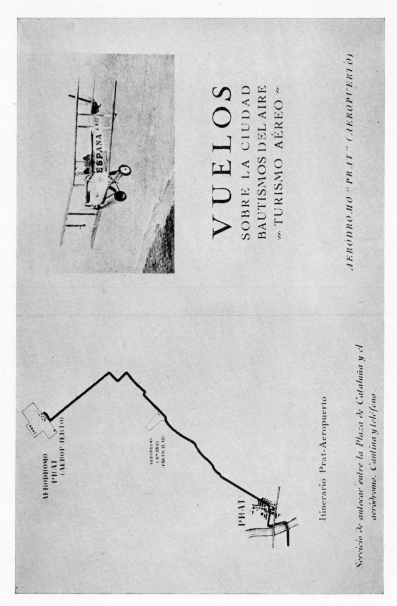

VUELOS

SOBRE LA CIUDAD
BAUTISMOS DEL AIRE
«TURISMO AÉREO»

AERÓDROMO "PRAT" (AEROPUERTO)

Itinerario Prat-Aeropuerto

*Servicio de autocar entre la Plaza de Cataluña y el
aeródromo. Cantina y teléfono.*

AERODROMO
PRAT
(AEROPUERTO)

AERODROMO
CANDAL
PUERTO-BAJO

PRAT

Publicity circular employed by Anton and Franz Josef to promote sightseeing flights over Barcelona.

Chapter Twenty-One

THE WIDOWED INFANTA continued to live on in Spain.

It was a tribute to her adaptability and enlightened modernism that she remained a welcome citizen under the new republic of Niceto Alcalá Zamora. Following Alfonso's abdication, all persons of royal complexion had removed themselves (or been forcibly removed) from the country. But the Archduke Leopold Salvator had been pointed out in Barcelona streets as the "democratic Habsburg," whose daughters went to market and did housework, while his sons thought nothing of taking jobs as garage mechanics. Yes, the imperial household of Sarriá belonged in the new Spain.

By the time his father died, Franz Josef had been graduated from the Peritaje Industrial de Tarrasa and the Barcelona School of Agriculture, situated in Calle Urgel, in addition to passing his tests as a licensed pilot under the Aeronáutica Naval (Marine Flying School) which accepted civilian students.

His problem, like that of Anton, who had recently returned from England, was how to obtain a plane. Commercial air lines were not sufficiently developed to expand their personnel, and the army and navy had pilots of their own. Thus the brothers, who were the first Habsburgs in history to earn their wings, remained grounded.

This suited the Infanta perfectly, for her modernism did not embrace aviation. As a bride she had trembled when her husband purchased his balloon, the justly famed *Meteor,* and with it made a number of perilous ascents. The thought that her own sons longed to take up where their intrepid parent had left off troubled her acutely. On the day that Franz Josef passed his flier's examination she received him with a grim announcement:

"I shall keep my mourning weeds handy, since you are bent on giving me reason to wear them!"

This left no doubt about one point: Mama was not to be inveigled into any contribution toward the purchase of a plane. If the boys hoped to own one it would have to be through their own efforts. They must work and pool their funds.

The prospect did not dampen their spirits, for they were bursting with enterprise. In London, Anton had learned English. He now obtained employment with a British concern, the London Standard Electric Company, engaged in drying up the notorious *marismas* (marshes) of the Guadalquivir near Seville. The work was rough and necessitated living in tents on the edge of steaming malaria-infested swamplands. But Anton had a special incentive for braving hardships in his effort to possess a plane. Some time ago, at a reception in the Palacio de Pedralbes, home of the Count Juán Antonio of Guëll, he had met Princess Ileana of Romania who—with her mother and brother Nicholas— had returned from a trip to America.

While talking with Anton, Ileana was still aglow with her impressions of the New World. She had seen an industrial empire, with skyscraper cities, golden prairies, majestic mountains, and a horizon of unlimited opportunity. She had danced with stalwart young cadets of West Point and Culver Military Academy, among whom she recalled Lieutenant William J. Glasgow, Captain Henry L. Douglas, Regimental Commander N. D. Knight, and C. C. Culver, grandson of the Academy founder. Collectively and individually these swains had initiated her into the delights of baseball, ice-cream sodas, and a hamburger on a bun. In short, her visit to the United States lent Ileana an added fascination which no other European girl of Anton's acquaintance possessed. He found her irresistible. He fell in love.

His problem was of course geography. The Royal Palace at Bucharest was hardly within calling distance for a suitor with a job in Spain. Unless he got himself a plane, Anton felt certain that one of her American beaux would manage to see Ileana first and pick her off.

Franz Josef's urge to fly was not motivated by romance, though he too happened to be sighing for a member of the fair sex. But the lady of his heart was within easy reach, necessitating no airplane wings for distant travels. She could be seen daily on his walk to and from work at the Barcelona Ford Plant, where he put stuffing in upholstery and tacked imitation leather linings onto bare body frames. Occasionally a tack was hammered into the archducal thumb, as the pangs of love became too much to bear—for Franz Josef's infatuation was hopeless from the start. The object of his adoration happened to be a Chilean matron named Teresa Sanfuentes de Sañiartú, who was happily married and had a daughter his own age. Unlike Anton, the lovelorn Franz Josef should have had a plane to get away from his romance.

It was the American manager of the Ford Plant, one Sam Murray, who in the end aided the brothers in the realization of their dream. Pointing out to them the value of a new field of enterprise, modern advertising, he encouraged Anton and Franz Josef to solicit employment as stunt fliers for a group of firms, his own included.

"You can hire a plane," said the sanguine Mr. Murray, "and pay for it in no time."

The idea was enormously appealing. It not only opened the way to a lucrative future, but for Anton an escape was offered from the mosquito plague of the Guadalquivir. Without a promising business venture awaiting him in the north, Anton would have remained stubbornly at his Seville job. Only an attractive project such as Franz Josef, with the promptings of Mr. Murray, now outlined to him could lure the older brother away.

The first ship flown by the two archdukes was hired from a commercial company at an exorbitant fee, which swallowed their combined earnings a full month in advance. But they started almost immediately to take orders for aerial photographs of real-estate developments, accident scenes, fires, dust storms, or even a particularly fine sunset. These pictures were sold to magazines like *El Día Gráfico,* as well as to insurance companies and housing agents. In addition the resourceful brothers acquired a smoke-producing device with which to engage in skywriting, not only above Barcelona but as far south as Madrid.

As their reputation grew, their earnings increased, so that before long the goal was realized: they owned their first airplane. An innovation could now be attempted, namely sight-seeing flights over the city and to the heights of Monserrat, for all who had the price of a ticket. Needless to say, Franz Josef's most ardent passenger (gratis, to be sure) was Old Vicente, who nowadays had nothing but contempt for such mediocre forms of locomotion as motorcycle sidecars or automobiles.

"At last," declared Vicente, who suffered from gout and found it increasingly hard to get around, "I have found the only fitting way to visit *La Patrona.*"

He went to Monserrat thereafter only on wings.

For Anton the Grail lay elsewhere. He had heard that

Queen Marie of Romania was visiting with Ileana at Freiburg-in-Breisgau, on the estate of a relative, Prince Friedl Hohenzollern-Sigmaringen. Impatient to see the girl again, Anton toyed with the thought of taking off on an unscheduled flight across France to southern Germany. But there was Franz Josef to be reckoned with. If Anton went off on a cruise above Prince Friedl's castle, who was to do the skywriting for the Sunday crowds gathered at the Barcelona racetrack? No, while they had only one ship between them there was no time for unprofitable excursions. Suspicious of his brother's intent, Franz Josef hovered forever about the precious lone plane upon which rested the fate of their "business." He busied himself with endless tasks at the hangar, inspecting, greasing, polishing. Indeed, there were times when he was not above removing some vital pin or bolt, so as to thwart a surprise take-off during those hours when perforce he must go home to sleep. For the rest, his every waking minute seemed devoted to the task of playing nursemaid to the cherished machine no less than to the effort of keeping Anton on the ground.

Throughout this time the two archdukes saved their pesetas with a vengeance. Having only one thought in mind —the purchase of a second plane—they practiced economy to the point of stinginess. To save cleaning bills each played valet to the other, fetching home gasoline for removal of spots, and doing a creditable job at pressing their own pants. They wore their clothes so threadbare that no ragpicker rang the doorbell of the house in Sarriá, as anything discarded by the flying archdukes was past redemption. In short, the brothers cut financial corners wherever possible, even stretching the interval between trips to the barber.

"The Paderewski twins!" said Mama disapprovingly, as

she observed the untidy hairline at the back of her sons' necks.

But they were not to be deterred from their object. And in the end their countless petty sacrifices added up to a gratifying result. The new plane, a shiny De Havilland-Moth two-seater, became at last a reality.

Its maiden voyage culminated unhappily in a crash. Through oversight by a factory inspector the plane had a faulty gauge which caused a miscalculation of fuel needs. Flying over France in midwinter, the archdukes headed into a snowstorm when their gasoline gave out despite the indicator showing the tank to be one-fourth full. They were already over their destination, Dijon, but could not coast the full distance to the airport beyond the town. With a dead motor they must make a forced landing and make it instanter. On ice-encrusted wings they circled an old parade ground known as the Champs de la Maladière, which had been transformed into a real-estate development, though there were still some empty lots between the encroaching houses. The largest of these lots might make a safe landing space, provided the plane could descend sharply and sweep lengthwise across the ground.

Planning to do just this, Franz Josef, who was at the controls, spotted a man on a bicycle idling casually across the field. To avoid hitting him it became necessary to make a sharp turn and slip down over one wing so as to shorten the angle of landing.

A further and disastrous hazard now presented itself in the form of an unfinished canalization ditch, stretching over the width of the field and blanketed by a deceptive crust of ice and snow. Scraping the housetop of Number 17, Rue de Ruffé (one of the new streets bordering on the de-

velopment) the plane tore off its landing gear and crashed
into the ditch.

At sight of the accident the cyclist was roused from his
serenity. Reminded that he was trespassing on private property, he pedaled swiftly away, lest he be held as a witness
and fetched into court.

By the time police and rescue squads arrived, Anton had
crawled from the debris, but Franz Josef lay unconscious
under the wreckage. It was only thanks to the empty gasoline tank that the ship had not burst into flame. Thus the
brothers escaped with broken noses and a slight concussion.

In vindication of their efficiency as pilots, the De Havilland factory cleared the flying archdukes of all responsibility. After thorough investigation into the disaster the fault
was placed squarely on the shoulders of the plane inspector,
who not only had neglected testing the gauge but also mis-
computed the motor's fuel needs and recorded this error in
the log book. As the tank showed no leak, even after the
crash, the evidence spoke for itself.

Accordingly, the machine was rebuilt free of cost and
shipped back to the archdukes, this time in perfect condition.

The experience had in no way dampened Franz Josef's or
Anton's ardor. Flying had become an all-consuming passion, not to be tempered by mishaps. On the contrary, they
felt that hereafter they would be able to make a forced landing inside a box, for the lesson of Dijon encouraged them to
study glider technique and to pass their examinations in this
branch of aviation as well.

Of course there was still the bee of romance in Anton's
bonnet, and soon he could be held back no longer. Descending upon Freiburg from the skies, he won Ileana by storm.
The engagement was announced that spring, followed by a

summer wedding at Castle Pelesch in Sinaïa, the mountain retreat of the Romanian sovereigns.

As for Franz Josef's far more complicated love affair, it led to a less happy ending. The South American lady who had won his heart returned unexpectedly to her home overseas.

"Don't follow me there," she had joked with the infatuated youth, "because when you meet my daughter you will ask me to become your mother-in-law!"

He grieved over these taunts which revealed that he had not been taken seriously. Perhaps he ought to launch an impassioned correspondence that would bear witness to his ardor and cause the cool beauty to return remorsefully to Spain. But letters, especially the amorous kind, took time. With Anton off on his honeymoon, Franz Josef practically lived at the Barcelona Airport, Prat del Llobregat, continuing the advertising stunts singlehanded and keeping up the popular sight-seeing flights. Where was he to find time for a literary love affair?

Of course, there remained always the telegraph. Europe too had lately adopted the American motto "Wire, don't write!" which not only saved labor but presented the additional advantage of conveying a sentiment while it was still reasonably fresh. But there was the economic angle once again. To keep the cables sizzling across the seas called for greater cash reserves than Franz Josef possessed.

There was also another obstacle, though minor in character. The Infanta Blanca had an incorrigible penchant for opening everybody's mail. This idiosyncrasy had long been accepted in the family circle without too much ill humor. Mama meant no harm. But, having indulged her pleasure for innocent snooping, she mislaid opened letters and frequently lost them altogether, since (to her, at least) they

Archduke Anton and family.

Archduke Carlos and his wife Christa.

were of no further interest. This left the original addressee in something of a fog. Certainly the hazards confronting Franz Josef's romance were not helped by the chance of interception on his mother's part.

It happened that not long after the departure of Señora de Sañiartú, the pining Archduke received an unsigned clipping from a Chilean newspaper. It was an obituary. The woman he adored with such juvenile fervor had reached home barely in time to die of a sudden heart attack.

He grieved extravagantly, for he was of an age when there is savor only in extremes. With the aid of a colleague from the Ford Plant, one Nicolás Casina, who played Chopin very well, Franz Josef gave himself over to sorrow in the grand and classic manner. He wept for a whole year. This was not always easy, as any emotion sustained to the point of routine loses in intensity. But with the sympathetic Nicolás at the piano, and a beaker of Málaga wine within reach, the tears could always be induced to flow.

From pain is born philosophy.

"Rejoice," said Nicolás, caressing a nocturne. "Blessed are they who know unhappiness in love!"

Franz Josef looked up, intrigued. "Why?" he asked, eager to extract the utmost torment from his misery.

The music soared, then fell to a hush, as Nicolás worded a pithy answer.

"Happy love ends with fulfilment. When the top is reached one can only descend——"

"Yes," agreed Franz Josef, somewhat befuddled by his friend's obscure meaning.

Nicolás finished on a note of hyperbole. "Unhappy love lives on forever, because it remains forever unfulfilled!"

It was an inspiring thought, nobly expressed. It also did

full justice to the memory of a beauteous lady, now eternally out of reach. In short, the Archduke Pepi had discovered one of the sweet rewards of frustration: by not getting what he wanted his capacity for wishing had increased a thousandfold.

Chapter Twenty-Two

THROUGHOUT HER LIFE the Infanta Blanca had been greatly concerned with the subject of inheritance. Being related to some of Europe's leading and most prolific dynasties, she had been trained early to survey what her material assets were likely to be. She was descended from kings and she counted ancestral riches as her natural dower; but there were also collateral bequests to be expected from uncles, aunts, cousins, sisters, or brothers. Royal fortunes were in a state of constant flux as each generation enjoyed a temporary stewardship over the tribal substance.

It was through her father, Don Carlos, that the Infanta had received the Italian property known as Tenuta Reale at Viareggio. Through her brother Jaime, on the other hand, she had fallen heiress to Castle Frohsdorf, ten kilometers from Mayerling, where the expatriate grandee had spent long years of exile.

The Archduke Leopold Salvator too had left behind sizable estates, among these the lordly castle of Hernstein near Wiener Neustadt, with its 15,000 acres of forest land crowned by the historic ruins of Emmaberg and Starhemberg. In addition there was the Palais Toscana in Vienna.

On paper all this counted as great wealth, invariably reverting to collective family ownership as individual members were cut off by death. But there is an ironic angle to royal riches. In time of political trouble, dynastic property is at the mercy of all comers; expropriation becomes the corollary to every change of regime, whether bloody or otherwise.

It is this uncertainty regarding tomorrow which lends royal personages their shifting, unstable character. However rightful and legalized their ownership of property may be, it remains insecure and subject to seizure at the slightest caprice of fate. No peasant would stand for such infringement upon his inherited claims; but unlike peasants and the solid *bourgeoisie,* royalty has no roots. From time immemorial dynasts have figured in the history of nations as actors on a richly accoutered stage, wearing their lavish tinsel while the crowd cheered, yet knowing all the while that the performance could be called off on short notice from the box office. Early in life a prince who is born to rule learns from his tutors and generally pessimistic kin that he may just as likely wind up as doorman or headwaiter in some hospitable foreign land.

No one knew this better than the Infanta Blanca, whose immediate ancestors had lived for generations in exile. The fact that she owned half a dozen castles on as many points of the European map did not put food on her table. For some years now she had not even held a key to one of her palatial front doors.

Under President Dr. Michael Hainisch and his Cabinet Minister Dr. Ignaz Seipel, the Austrian Republic had gradually relaxed the decrees of banishment against members of the imperial family. On his death the Archduke Leopold Salvator had even been honored by a funeral procession through Vienna streets and burial in the Capuchin Monastery.

The same was true of Rainer, whose unexpected death from blood poisoning came within a few months of Papa's. Through Rainer the Infanta received title to the estate of Isdebnitz in Poland, with its great timberlands and *Schlibowitz* distillery. But this too constituted purely nominal possession, as she had no means of hacking wood or bottling a single dram of the famed schnapps.

In short, gestures of the above sort, however courteous, did not mean money in the bank. The Infanta and her children had still no wherewithal to open a single *Schloss* that might be restored to her name.

This called for no lament, either on her part or that of her offspring. Austria had undergone ruinous hardships in the years following the war; during 1922-1923, when inflation was at its peak, a restaurant meal cost 53,000 kronen, and swarms of Vienna children wasted away from malnutrition. It would have been monstrous under those conditions even to dream of the old luxurious life.

With the presidency of Wilhelm Miklas, in 1929, and the subsequent chancellorship of Dr. Engelbert Dollfuss, matters improved. Austria had been accepted into the League of Nations, and foreign loans helped relieve the most crying distress. But this did not augur a return of imperial splendors. The palaces of the Habsburgs remained unoccupied.

The Infanta Blanca viewed these facts with the cool eye of logic. She had long ago found out that inherited goods gave one no sense of possession, but merely of temporary tenure. No sooner did some aging relative bequeath his earthly chattels to surviving heirs than those heirs must rewrite their wills and arrange for future disposal of the entrusted boon.

"Only what you have worked for," said the Infanta, "really belongs to you!"

It was in keeping with this thought that she prized the Tenuta Reale at Viareggio as the one tangible possession from which she dared claim an income. For this Italian property was not a pleasure palace, but a productive estate growing the best grapes in Tuscany. It had been operated, first by Don Carlos and later by the archducal family, on the principle of *mezzadria* or equal-share basis between the peasants who worked the land and the owners who supervised it.

The manor house itself was simple and unpretentious, set on the flatlands that fronted a wide stretch of beach and the deeply blue Ligurian Sea. In the haze beyond the farthest breakers lay the island of Elba, while in the opposite direction the terrain sloped upward toward the famed marble hills of Carrara.

Originally the soil of Tenuta Reale had not been productive, due to the combination of salt air and ocean-washed silt. But by determined effort the ground had been fertilized and enriched, so that an avenue of pines grew to the very beach, sheltering the house against stormy winds. The trees also provided a screen for the great vineyards that were planted from American seed imported from California, which brought, in good times, an annual profit of half a million lire. An aging major-domo named Giuseppe Ferrari, descended from the overseers who had served Don Carlos, was currently in charge. It was from him that the Infanta Blanca obtained spasmodic reinforcement for her slender purse.

Money from Tenuta Reale had made it possible for the family to attend Anton's wedding at Castle Pelesch, with a Paris visit thrown in on the homeward trip. Mama loved France and French *esprit*. As a girl she had attended school in Florence, where everyone had seemed to her unutterably stodgy and dull. Later, when Paris lent a finishing touch to her education, the contrast had been unforgettable. She found the French clever, witty, resourceful, and always amusing. This was true even of the nuns in the Sacré Coeur: at Florence they were as depressingly ascetic as their counterparts in Barcelona or Madrid, while Paris nuns were somehow "Parisian."

While traveling, Mama preserved rigorous incognito. She called herself Madame Navarre, Señora Martínez, or Frau Mayer, according to the dictates of the moment. For the Romanian journey and the subsequent French visit the first of these aliases was chosen, though in passing through Vienna she changed momentarily to Mayer. This was due to a small accident that befell her on a corner of the Kärntnerstrasse. While rushing from one railroad station to another the Infanta ripped her string of pearls. As the precious beads rolled across the sidewalk and people stooped to pick them up, she had a sudden fear of being robbed. In a flash of inspiration she introduced herself (a crowd had begun to form) as Frau Mayer from Innsbruck.

"Don't bother," she squealed, pretending vast amusement, "those aren't real pearls—my husband bought them for a schilling!"

As she walked on with a great show of indifference, public interest diminished. Only her daughters remained behind to scramble after each priceless pellet.

In Paris a different adventure befell Mama, which ended less happily. She had miscalculated expenses and found herself embarrassingly short of funds. Knowing that the faithful Ferrari would not let her down, she wired to Viareggio for a loan of ten thousand lire. In wording her telegram, however, she employed figures instead of spelling out the sum, thus:

"Prego manda subito 10,000 lire."

By doing this she had saved one franc, but such economy was to cost her dearly. Through some error on the telegraphist's part the figure was swelled by another zero, reading 100,000 lire. The administrator at Tenuta Reale frantically tore his hair. What manner of catastrophe could have befallen Her Imperial and Royal Highness to necessitate so big a sum? He did not for a minute suspect a misprint or clerical error. When aristocrats needed help, it was never of a paltry character. Though it might be only the Infanta's hotel bill which called for settlement, Ferrari came to the rescue as if an empire were at stake. By pledging next year's crop, he raised the requested money and wired it forthwith to France.

In Paris the Infanta was delighted to receive tenfold the amount she had asked for.

"My," she remarked to her daughters, "things must be prospering at Viareggio!"

Wishing to safeguard a tidy nest egg, she withdrew the money from her bank, where she was known as the Archduchess Leopold Salvator, to deposit it elsewhere under one of her pseudonyms. This, she felt, would be a protection against the countless charity requests that were addressed to her by people who believed the fiction of her inexhaustible wealth. "As the daughter of Don Carlos," petitioners prefaced their appeals, "you have become heiress to the greatest fortunes of Spain. . . ." Indeed, there were those who vowed she owned the ancient treasure of the Montezumas, if not a store of legendary Inca gold, supposedly transported to Madrid in the days of the *Conquistadores*.

Well, as Madame Navarre she planned to keep a little cash where no one, not even her children, knew about it.

Carrying the money in her *pochette*—which resembled nothing so much as a midwife's well-worn satchel—the Infanta set out for one of the shabbier Paris sectors, where she hoped to find an obscure but dependable bank. To save the cost of a taxi she went on foot, clutching the bag feverishly under one arm.

At last, in some unfamiliar *faubourg,* she came upon the branch offices of a banking firm she had never heard of before. This was just what she wanted. If she herself did not know the place, how could anyone else suspect that she had money there?

By now she was completely fascinated with her project. Why not add mystification by discarding her customary aliases and inventing something quite new? That was it: she would make her deposit under some outlandish name no one had ever heard of!

This performance took only a few minutes. A short while later the Infanta emerged into the street once more, armed with a small bank receipt and checkbook. Pleased with herself, she made a concession to economy and boarded a tram which carried her swiftly back to the center of town.

It was only on arrival at her hotel that she discovered a ghastly mishap. She had lost both checkbook and deposit slip, together with the name and address of the bank. What was worse, she could not for the life of her remember the new alias she had employed. In her passion for secrecy she had succeeded in hoodwinking everybody, including the one person most vitally concerned—herself.

Luckily she had retained enough cash to pay her bill and get safely back to Spain. But the problem that now confronted her was how to track down the misplaced funds. Could she tell her children and expose herself to endless ridicule? This, she felt, was almost worse than losing the money.

In the end she decided to compromise by writing her son Leopold, who was in Vienna and at least did not have to be met face to face with so preposterous a tale. On paper she gave Leopold the facts, closing with an abashed question. Did he think he could do anything?

Leopold welcomed the chance to be of service, for he had of late caused some eyebrow-raising among his numerous kin. This was due to domestic troubles. His marriage to Dagmar had gone on the rocks during the same year of 1931 which had been marked by so many significant events —the abdication of Alfonso; the deaths of Rainer, Papa, and Don Jaime; the coming of age (at Steenockerzeel) of the Pretender, Archduke Otto; and lastly, Anton's Romanian wedding.

What caused family frowns was the fact that Leopold's union with the Croatian baroness had been dissolved, not by annulment—hardly possible, since there was a daughter, Gabrielle—but through the modern channel of divorce. Among strictly Catholic Habsburgs this was an unseemly innovation.

Mama, of course, had frowned with particular severity. This made her present predicament the more poignant, since she must make the humiliating admission that she alone was to blame for the egregious bloomer with the Paris bank. Leopold would say—and rightly—that she had not been very intelligent. But as he had temporarily problems of his own, his criticism would be easier to bear. In turning to him she felt that spontaneous affinity which springs up between people, alien or related, who happen to be in trouble. Dear Leopold. She was sure he would help.

He certainly tried. With such data as Mama could give him—namely that she had forgotten the neighborhood, the bank, and the pseudonym she had used, besides losing the checkbook and deposit slip—he went to work. It was not much to go on. Or rather, it was exactly nothing. But suddenly Leopold had a brilliant flash. Did Mama remember the date of the transaction, and the day of the week? With this clue one could have the books of every Paris bank examined until an entry of approximately 90,000 lire was located.

Alas, the Infanta seldom looked at calendars. And as for the days of the week, since she attended Mass each morning, even Sunday seemed to her indistinguishable from any other time.

In view of the above, Leopold could scarcely be blamed for throwing up his hands. No amount of deduction could succeed where reason itself had been so conspicuously lacking. The net result was that the money borrowed from Viareggio remained forever lost.

As for Mama, she had simply proved what the family knew all the time. She was a true Infanta: a grandee of the old school, as removed from practical living as Rapunzel in her tower. Her one excursion into the field of high finance bore the stamp of utter and disarming caprice.

Though she was a lady of the world, Mama could not be called worldly.

Chapter Twenty-Three

THE SPANISH REPUBLIC, set up after the downfall of King Alfonso XIII, was not the much heralded Utopia that its supporters had been led to expect. Its leadership rested in the hands of competent men like Alcalá Zamora, Miguel Maura, Gil Robles, as well as army heads like Sanjurjo, Mola, Queipo de Llano, Batet, and Godet. Collectively these patriots were prepared to serve Democracy with every power at their command, though individually they differed in their approach. In the group no fewer than six political philosophies were represented: Conservatism, Socialism, Marxism, Anarcho-Syndicalism (trade-unionism), Communism, and even a modified Monarchism (presumably reformed according to the British pattern).

Beyond a doubt Spain was getting its first taste of a genuine attempt at liberal government. But the wrongs from which the nation suffered, and had been suffering for centuries past, were not to be cured by a simple change from tyranny to parliamentary procedure. For one thing, enormous economic reforms were called for, since the bulk of Spain's lower classes continued to live in the abject poverty they had known under Bourbon rule. Part of this poverty was directly attributable to the power of the Church and the scant knowledge transmitted through its parochial schools. It served the interests of a particularly narrow Spanish clericalism to keep the masses meek and uninformed, concerned only with the glory of the Kingdom of Heaven.

Spiritually considered, this was a tenable philosophy, provided one could count on being only briefly for this earth.

But with a normal span of life to be lived through, the hereafter paled beside the stringencies of a hard present. Spain's humble classes, tired of frugality, were demanding higher wages, better education, and three square meals a day. They had been stirred up by the forces of modern industrialism and by the development throughout the western world of labor representation.

This was bad news to Spain's leading stockholders, the clerics, who in 1932 controlled sixty percent of the country's industry, including public utilities, dams, reservoirs, mines, and engineering schools. Fundamentally Monarchist, the Church had disowned Alfonso and voted for the Republic so as to safeguard these valuable interests. But now a new threat loomed on the horizon as increasingly radical elements in the Zamora government urged far-reaching reforms. Most Leftist measures smacked of ultimate expropriation.

To arrest such trends, Catholic leaders formed an active lobby in Madrid. At election time they made it clear that all Conservative candidates could count on an avalanche of clerical votes, a promise which was backed by ample financial support.

It was on the crest of this reactionary wave that an obscure militarist named Francisco Franco rose to power and dreamed an ancient dream of personal aggrandizement.

The postwar fashion for psychoanalysis had something to do with it. A prostrate Europe had been told by Jung, Adler, and Freud that it suffered from an inferiority complex —which was undoubtedly true. The remedy for this uncomfortable state, so the learned professors said, lay in refusing to recognize it. That is, the cause of one's inferiority must be uncovered, aired, and dismissed in short order, while the "will to superiority" was planted in its place.

Through some mental alchemy—perhaps best exemplified in the pseudo-psychological pap spouted by Dr. Coué—a metamorphosis was supposedly accomplished. The era of Nietzsche's Superman was thus practically guaranteed to be on the way.

This school of thought, subscribed to by most "short-cut-to-success" prophets, had already borne fruit. In 1922 a frustrated Italian socialist had thrust out his chin and marched on Rome, impersonating Caesar. Ten years later his Germanic counterpart, with a bad haircut and a laughable mustache, was winning friends and influencing people by putting the same formula to use. According to the proverb, all good things were three. Francisco Franco was of the same opinion.

Actually Franco must be regarded less of an upstart than either Mussolini or Hitler. He had a better pedigree. Yet, despite acceptable family background and educational advantages, he had achieved no distinction as a soldier. The future looked even less promising. Unless, of course, one did something about it.

To stir up anti-democratic feeling in a country as feudal as Spain was not a difficult matter. The nobility as well as the moneyed gentry trembled before one bugaboo, Bolshevism. If they could be made to feel that the present Republic was but a step to ultimate Sovietization, the gamble was won. Men of property had but one answer when asked to choose between Communism and almost anything else. Franco offered them his *Falange*.

Since Mussolini called himself *Il Duce* and Hitler had become *Der Fuehrer,* the Spanish leader too longed for a proper sobriquet. He hit upon *El Caudillo,* the ancient word for chieftain. It had a gallant ring.

In addition Franco had the advantage of springing from

a well-known Catholic house. His own seeming devoutness
aroused confidence among people who, though indifferent
to politics, wished to preserve cherished traditions and a stable way of life. Many of Spain's best families were thus
misguided into supporting the embryo dictator.

At this point an unexpected factor came to Franco's aid,
though it is doubtful that he really needed it. The success or
failure of the new Republic depended entirely upon its ability to conciliate and satisfy the working classes. This meant
a prompt rise in wages without corresponding increase of
unemployment, and the immediate passage of agrarian reforms. Due to inexperience, and the intrinsic slowness of
democratic procedure, the Zamora government made little
headway with the urgent legislation. As a result the impatient Socialist leader, Largo Caballero, called a general strike
in Madrid to celebrate Europe's Day of Labor, the first of
May. At the head of ten thousand workers he led a procession through the principal streets, saluting with clenched
fist, and waving a banner with the inscription:
"We want a Workers' Government. Long live the Red
Army!"

Nothing could have played more conveniently into
Franco's hand. Liberals who up to now had hesitated to
align themselves with anything of even faint Fascist odor
began to waver. Here was a new and terrifying danger, the
fist of Moscow overshadowing Spain! Perhaps they had better swing back to the Right before it was too late. . . .

Ultimately it was the religious question, however, which
drove the greatest number of followers into the Franco
camp. After the tactical mistake of Largo Caballero, radical
elements in remote provincial districts believed the Commune already established at Madrid. Acting on this assumption, they gave the signal for the sacking of churches,

convents, and monasteries in the best Russian fashion of the
day. It was a long-dormant compulsion to wreak revenge
upon a power that for centuries had failed in its true mission: the elevation of the poor and the practice of genuine
brotherhood. The venal Church, which had forgotten
Christ's Sermon on the Mount, was being thus chastised.

Without condoning these acts, it is an accepted fact that
Christianity has drifted far from its original source. A
British student of Spanish history, Mr. Gerald Brenan, says
in *The Spanish Labyrinth* (Macmillan, 1943):

"The reason for this violence [against the Church] is
obvious. The Bible, and especially the New Testament,
contains enough dynamite to blow up all the existing social
systems in Europe; only by force of habit and through the
power of beautiful and rhythmical words we have ceased to
notice it. An intelligent Chinaman has been more observant.
Sun Yat Sen, when he visited Europe, was amazed that a
religion which persistently extolled the poor and threatened
and condemned the rich should be practiced and maintained
chiefly by the richest, most selfish and most respectable
classes. The political skill and duplicity required for such a
feat seemed to him to go far beyond anything that simple
Orientals could run to. The danger has therefore always
existed that any weakening in the influence of the Church,
any desertion of the interests of the poor by the priesthood,
would lead to a greater emphasis being placed upon the
social principles of equality, voluntary poverty and brotherly
love that, along with many other things, lie at the root of
Christianity. . . ."

That the preachments of Jesus have been left far behind is
news to most formalized Christians who not only fail to live
by the spirit of the Gospel, but disregard even its letter. How
many contributions to God's cause represent the Biblical
"tithe" or one-tenth of the donor's earthly goods?

Yet formalized Christians throughout Spain were horrified

Franz Josef and Anton in their De Havilland Gypsy Moth: *"España."*

Crash of the De Havilland-Moth.

and incensed at the "blasphemous" attack inflicted upon the Church, forgetting that the attackers were not heathen, but Catholics too—the poorest, the Church's own disinherited.

In any case, here was the windfall Franco had waited for. Swept off their feet by mass hysteria as well as unvarnished propaganda from every pulpit in the land, the more devout elements in the country threw themselves into the Caudillo's arms.

"He is on the side of God!" they said.

And, outwardly at least, he certainly was.

In 1936, when the Spanish Civil War broke into open flame, Santiago Casares Quiroga was Prime Minister under the presidency of Manuel Azaña. José Calvo Sotelo, former Finance Minister under Primo de Rivera, headed the revived Monarchist party which currently sided with the Falange. But, what was far more significant, from Germany and Italy there had come a joint pledge of military help against the Red menace. Franco was ready to strike.

The Republic, for its part, had not been idle. It too had received offers, not from the democracies—England, France, or the Americas—but from Russia. The desperate are not choosers. In its life-and-death struggle the Azaña government took what help it could get, with the result that Spain became a testing ground for Nazi and Fascist armor against the might of the Kremlin.

From the start of hostilities the republican forces were handicapped by dissidence within their own ranks. Under the banner of democracy they hoped to reconcile ideologies that ranged from extreme Trotzkyism (proclaimed by the inflammatory Dolores Ibárruri, known as *La Pasionaria*) to a modified Socialism of the mildest sort. Adding to the confusion was the change undergone by Russia under her new leader, Josef Stalin. Communist elements in Spain still thought in terms of 1919, whereas the modern Comintern was a totalitarian regime ruled by a bureaucracy and operating in the strictest authoritarian fashion.

In Franco's camp there was no such discord. Enjoying the enormous moral support of the Church, the Falange united Monarchists, Conservatives, Reactionaries; in short, everyone who feared Liberalism or change of any sort. Finally, Franco's greatest help came from England, where the appeasement policy of Mr. Chamberlain was in full sway. The British Prime Minister urged noninterference in the internal affairs of Spain, not only for his own country but for France as well. This gave the Italians and the Germans a free hand.

Early in the war the Caballero government fell, following a clash with the trade unions of Catalonia, which led to a week of street fighting in Barcelona. The ousted officials were replaced by Indalecio Prieto as Minister of Defense, with Juan Negrín taking charge of the Republic's finances, and Julio Álvarez del Vayo acting as Foreign Minister.

But Stalin was losing interest in the struggle. The Kremlin had no wish to help implant elsewhere a brand of Bolshevism which it had long discarded at home. Under Stalin's guidance the Communist system had undergone such modifications that modern Russia could no longer identify herself with the chaotic collectivism of Trotzky and Lenin. In addition, there was the growing difficulty of transporting military supplies to Spain across Axis-dominated lands or nonco-operating British seas. Finally, Russia was learning on Spanish battlefields to gauge the full strength of the future German and Italian war machines, as well as the uncertain stand of the democracies, including America. Realist that he was, Stalin withdrew from the West to mend his own fences and prepare for a far greater struggle yet to come. Spain taught him to build up reserves for World War II.

With her sole sincere support no longer guaranteed by a staunch Muscovite champion, the Loyalist Republic perished sadly in March 1939.

Chapter Twenty-Four

IN THE TURMOIL of Spain's Civil War the Barcelona Habsburgs were scattered far and wide.

They had survived Alfonso's abdication, adjusting themselves to the requirements of the subsequent Republic. All of them, with the possible exception of Mama, had ceased to be royalty; they had become part of a working work-a-day world. Life in the comfortable house at Sarriá might have continued unchanged, since no threat of banishment hung over the heads of its wage-earning occupants. But the sheer violence of the fratricidal war that tore through the Spanish Peninsula caused numerous families to seek refuge beyond the country's borders. With hoodlumism rampant on the streets, and churches set afire by the mob, it was but a step to the looting of private homes and destruction of all property. The Infanta Blanca and her children remembered similar events in Austria. They knew when it was time to go.

Ordinarily Mama could not be called a coward. She had the courage to face hardships without flinching. But widowhood had shaken her spirit. Alone, without a protective and devoted husband by her side, she found herself faltering. Nor could she lean too heavily upon her children, as most of them had married or flown from the roost to fend for themselves. There was Immaculata, wedded since 1932 to an Italian *nobile*, Igino Neri Serneri, while Margareta would soon become the bride of the Marchese Francesco Maria Taliani di Marchio. As for Maria Antonia, whose romance had high-lighted the Mallorcan visit of so many years ago, she was the happy mother of five children—four girls and a boy. There remained only Assunta, safely immured in her convent, and Dolores, who seemed destined for spinsterhood.

Of her five sons the Infanta now had two by her side, Franz Josef and Carlos. Rainer was dead. Anton had settled with Ileana at Mödling near Vienna, where their first child, Archduke Stefan, was born. As for Leopold, he had gone to America following his divorce.

It was strange, the Infanta reflected, how a family could dwindle. In the old days, with ten children crowding the nursery, she had sometimes wondered if she would ever again know the luxury of being alone. Well, that time was almost here. And now she could not bear to face it—at least not here in Barcelona, where bloodshed and destruction had become the order of the day.

Where could she turn?

For some years past Austria's new Chancellor Schuschnigg had welcomed roaming Habsburgs back to their homeland. With Spain disrupted by revolution, the Infanta decided to return to Vienna.

Where would she live?

One of her husband's properties, the Palais Toscana, had been converted by the government into an apartment building. For a modest sum the widowed Archduchess Leopold Salvator would be able to rent a few of her former rooms.

This meant cramped quarters, hence only Dolores and Carlos stopped under the same roof. Franz Josef in any case was branching out in the profession he had learned to love: advertising. He went directly to Paris, where he found part-time work in the tourist promotion departments of two rival air lines, the Dutch and the French. In addition he prepared posters and travel circulars for international automobile clubs as well as the ubiquitous cyclist organizations that infested the Continent. Here was a field of great promise during a decade when European travel would mount to its peak.

Back in Barcelona, meanwhile, only the girl Soledad remained to guard the house of her former masters and to face the ordeal of the Spanish War.

Life's values had become confused for Soledad. Staunchly republican by heritage, she had—against her own will—grown attached to the unroyal royalties whom she found so easy to serve. In the house at Sarriá all her anti-monarchist convictions had somehow faded into foolish prejudice. A ménage of imperial highnesses who polished their own boots and tidied up after themselves was so out of keeping with the accepted picture of dynastic conduct that Soledad found herself politically at sea. If humility could dwell in high places, what would be left for class-hatred to feed on?

To confound her spirit further, she had been forced to become a member of the Domestic Workers' Union, since Catalonia was strongly Syndicalist and wished its labor elements to be properly organized. Part of the union's purpose was to ascertain through its members whether reactionary Rightist forces were at work in private homes, plotting against the government. Like thousands of her comrades in domestic service, Soledad was expected to spy on her unsuspecting employers.

It was an irksome and distasteful task. If in all Spain people had minded their own affairs as decently as the occupants of the house in Sarriá, the Republic would certainly have flourished forever. Of this much Soledad was sure. No matter how often she was summoned to the examiners' board, she had nothing of consequence to report beyond the fact that the Infanta and her daughters dispensed with beauty parlors by wearing paper curlers in their hair, while the young archdukes donned American overalls to cut down on their tailoring bills.

Among more rabid Syndicalists such information had been received with distrust. But Soledad had the support of Pablo Riba, the son of Old Vicente. During the uprising against the King, Pablo had joined the republican forces and remained in military service under the Zamora and Azaña governments. In Soledad's eyes Pablo was a hero. They planned to marry, once the war was over and peace returned to Spain. It was a dream which Soledad owed likewise to her royal employers, for she had met Pablo through his fellow garage worker, the Archduke Pepi. The youth had stopped by one morning to give Franz Josef a lift in his truck. For Soledad, sweeping up the front path, it had been only a brief exchange of glances, without the passing of a single word. But Pablo had come back often after that, and the Archduke Pepi obtained many a free ride while love blossomed under his unwitting nose.

It had been partly due to the garage hand's friendship and the housemaid's loyalty that the Infanta and her family had continued unmolested until the very eve of the Civil War. If ever a breath of suspicion attached itself to the Sarriá household, it was enough that a soldier of the Republic and a union member of good standing rose to the family's instant defense.

With the outbreak of hostilities, however, no further protection would have been possible. Bombs would rain down on Spanish cities, heeding no caste or creed. Even the poorest of the poor were ordered to evacuate their hovels and flee to safety in country districts. Tearfully the Infanta bade farewell to Doña Sol, as she continued to call the orphan girl who had been so many years in her service. For Soledad stayed on. Pablo was one of the city's defenders against the onmarching Falange. So long as he remained in Barcelona, Soledad would not leave.

One other former member of the Sarriá household did not think of flight. This was the Archduchess Assunta, now a full-fledged nun in the Order of the Teresianas.

They had all been mistaken about Assunta. She had not been a victim of self-deception or religious mania, as everyone was always so ready to believe. Quite serenely she had found her niche in accord with the vocation she so ardently professed. The period of her novitiate had been marked by no doubt or regret, just as, at the time she was ordained, no one saw her waver as her luxurious dark tresses were shorn off and laid upon the altar.

Yes, in Spain's hour of travail all who could find means of escape sped off to safety. But there were those who stayed behind: Soledad for love, Assunta for her faith.

As the war progressed it became obvious that faith in general and the Catholic Church in particular would undergo grave trials. Enraged at Franco's clerical support, the republican forces launched their policy of incendiarism and destruction of ecclesiastic properties. Wherever resistance was encountered the aroused rabble gave way to savagery and bestial instinct, adding torture, rape, and murder to their crimes. It was the story of the French Terror and the Russian Commune all over again.

At the Convent of the Teresianas measures had been taken months ago in preparation for the day when disaster might strike. Civilian clothes had been smuggled in and stored away, not only for fugitive priests who had found refuge on the premises, but for the nuns as well. It had also been decreed by the Mother Superior that all members of the sisterhood must let their hair grow, so as to doff their coifs on short notice.

The dreaded hour was not long in arriving.

On December 16, 1936, Barcelona awoke to the sound of gunfire and street brawling. Crowds milled through the downtown sector bearing clubs and lighted torches.

"A acabar con el clero!" was the battle cry. ("Finish with the clergy!")

A short time later columns of smoke rose from pyres started in the rear of monasteries, churches, and other religious buildings, including the modernistic Templo de la Sagrada Familia. Had not the moment been too stark for persiflage, even the more pious Barcelona citizens would have admitted that the architectural incubus of Señor Gaudí deserved being consigned to flames, as it challenged every revered and classic style. But the current wave of destruction obeyed no aesthetic impulse: it was inspired by base passions and a fierce, uncontrolled lust. For the rioters did not stop at burning or looting. Taxis were commandeered and driven through the streets with priests dragging behind them over icy pavements, their heads crushed and their vestments spattered with mire and blood. Behind these came two-wheeled carts with women, some in tatters, others completely stripped; they were the nuns whose chastity became now an object for common sport. Catcalls and vile obscenities were hurled at the terrorized creatures who shivered in their nakedness, too harrowed even for tears.

From an upstairs window at Sarriá the girl Soledad looked down upon the incredible scene. Here were indeed the tumbrils of the French Revolution, which the Infanta Blanca had always talked about. Here was the Terror. Nothing could evoke its specter more poignantly than the sight of a shackled human being thump-thumping along in a two-wheeled cart. . . .

Soledad shuddered. White-lipped and chilled to the marrow, she stared, unable to accept the testimony of her eyes.

Was this the way to better a world that had been wronged by tyranny? Were such excesses not infinitely worse than anything they purported to combat? Surely no one in his right mind could count on a survival of the Republic through acts of infamy. What she beheld today hardly came under the head of fighting; it was raw, unadulterated crime.

Not for the first time, Soledad wondered about the excuse for war and for its cost in lives, tears, and treasure. From the financial angle alone was it not absurd? For the price of armies, navies, planes, tanks, and ammunition one could banish poverty from the earth. Yet who, in peacetime, was willing to *give* what during war is *taken* from him with his full and patriotic consent?

Was mankind so little creative that its contribution could be enlisted only for destructive purposes?

Her heart ached suddenly for Pablo, garrisoned in Barcelona as one of the citadel's "gallant" defenders. If today's deeds were a sample of that gallantry she wondered what horrors victory would bring.

It was not that her loyalty to Pablo wavered or that she could, even for a second, condone the Falangist uprising which had thrust Spain into civil war. She accepted Francisco Franco on no terms whatever. Aligned with the Church, El Caudillo desecrated no altars and his warrior horde deflowered no nuns; but cruelty was rampant in Franco prisons, where solitary confinement or the monotony of mass regimentation drove captives insane. If one must choose between two evils, perhaps the forthright vulgarity of Barcelona's *canaille* was more endurable.

One thing remained certain. Soledad could not compromise with dictatorship, even if religion stood ostensibly behind it. But by the same token she now felt a sickening presentiment of doom for the Republic which had allowed itself to be sidetracked from its primary humane purpose. Democracy, if it hoped to prevail over other political systems, must scorn their misdeeds, since no greater fallacy was ever uttered than that the end hallowed the means. As for a Free Spain, Soledad feared that this was not its day. A different kind of struggle, and vastly different men, would be needed to usher in its final triumph.

Even while she brooded behind her curtained window, the girl perceived that the mob now swung around a corner. She caught her breath with a gasp. The smoldering torches pointed straight for the Convent of the Teresianas, where the Archduchess Assunta was in hiding!

Instantly Soledad was galvanized into action. She must go out and find Pablo. He was at the barracks near Tibidabo, on guard with a regiment of sharpshooters. If she hurried to him he might surround the Teresianas with a cordon of men and protect the nunnery from a mob assault.

Wrapping a kerchief about her hair, she rushed into the street and pressed head-on against the roaring throng. She noticed now that the multitude was swelling in size as suburban crowds joined the main stream. Within a few minutes Soledad found herself stopped in her tracks, then swept off in the opposite direction. It was hopeless; she would never get to Pablo. The surging mass of pummeling, screaming creatures moved inexorably on to the very portals of the convent.

The great building lay in silence, shuttered against the world. At sight of its massive and dignified walls, the clamorous mob subsided momentarily. There was a hush of indecision, as though some signal must needs be awaited. All acts of collective violence called for the initiative of a single trigger force: the beast could not move without a head. It was immaterial who would throw the first rock that crashed through the chapel transept, or who might swing the blazing brand that ignited the roof. It mattered only that there was a rock and a first flash of flame.

The tossing hand happened to belong to a mere child, an overwrought boy of ten, but it electrified the crowd to renewed frenzy, redoubling the lost momentum. Stones rained against the convent windows now, followed by flares and improvised stink bombs, while here and there a few enterprising assailants began scaling the walls.

Within the structure panic reigned. In padded slippers the nuns raced from their cells and through the corridors, heading for the back stairs. At the far end of the convent gardens there was a small exit from which a curving lane ran across fields to the airport and the River Llobregat. If they could reach this path the frantic sisters vaguely hoped to take either to the water or to the clouds.

They were a grotesque sight, swarming around the Mother Superior like drones and working bees about their queen. All had discarded convent garb for worldly attire, yet they looked like nothing out of contemporary life. The raiment they had stored away against just this crisis had been purchased from a secondhand dealer who reasoned that nuns were unversed in matters of fashion, and so he could sell them a residue of shopworn leftovers. It was a cruel prank, as some of the dated styles came from a forgotten 1912 stock.

What added to the outlandish effect was the appearance of the nuns' heads, deprived now of a framing coif and veil. As many of the Teresianas were no longer young, their hair grew slowly and they had barely achieved an unruly stubble by the time their tops were bared. It did not help that the hats they now donned were of even older vintage than the atrocious dresses. If, in putting on civilian "disguise," the good ladies hoped to pass unnoticed in a crowd, they had been heartlessly deceived. In return for honest payment the garment dealer had transformed them into a travesty.

As the Mother Superior now scurried ahead of her flock, down winding passages and stairs, her beads clicked by her side. She was reciting one last rosary, entreating the heavens for help. After each *Ave Maria* she called on Saint Thérèse the Elder, patroness of the order.

It looked for a while as though these invocations would bear fruit, for at the back of the convent all appeared quiet. Noiselessly the bolt was lifted from the ivy-covered gate and the nuns slipped outside, stumbling over one another in their haste. But they were to meet with a disastrous surprise. At least fifteen minutes earlier a part of the milling crowd had sneaked to the rear of the convent and waited there in silence, ready to pounce on the unsuspecting fugitives. Stepping from the recess of their garden, the nuns found themselves encircled by the mob.

With a shriek the frantic sisters turned around, but it was too late. The gate had already been slammed shut behind them. They were engulfed and at the mercy of their captors. What followed was but a repetition of the outrages committed in other sectors of the martyred town, where lechery and sadism had been given full rein.

It was dusk of a gray day in the grayness of a Catalonian winter. The sky glowed orange and crimson, reflecting the fires that roared and crackled throughout the city. Yet the Convent of the Teresianas would not burn. Its ancient stone walls, reinforced by recent improvements at the hands of the architect Gaudi, resisted all incendiary attacks.

This drove the mob to fury. Pistols and guns were aimed at the stalwart building, while rocks and other missiles shattered every window in sight. On every side, except along the sacristy wing beyond the chapel, bullets came whistling through the air and peppered the structure with futile pock-marks. The sacristy, protected by a high parapet, lay forward in the wind which blew the flames of incendiary bombs and faggots in an opposite direction.

There was a door here, leading from the vestment room to the choir loft above the High Altar. As candles, censers, and other combustible material were stored in this part of the building, all exits had been equipped with fireproof panels.

It was in the shadow of the choir loft that a young woman stood motionless and alert. Her dark head, with hair grown in irregular wisps about a face of monastic pallor, left no doubt that she was a nun, though by some miracle she had missed taking part in the costume farce through which her hapless companions had hoped to make their escape. She wore a servant dress, complete with scarf and billowing apron borrowed from Doña Paz, the gardener's wife. By a still greater miracle, though surrounded by gunfire, she was alive and—as yet—unhurt.

Her baptismal name of Mary of the Ascension had been transposed, on consecration, to Sor María de Jesús Crucificado.

She had been known formerly as Her Imperial and Royal Highness, the Archduchess Assunta.

Chapter Twenty-Five

IT WAS NOT THROUGH FORESIGHT that she stood there apart from the rest and was spared the fate that had befallen them.

At the first alarm Assunta had rushed from her cell and joined the other nuns in their frantic descent to the garden. Being one of the youngest, her place had been near the end of the line, as older and less agile sisters must be assured the quickest chance of escape.

While the long queue moved forward, an appalling thought had struck Assunta. Sister Petra, a veteran nun who had retired from active duty, was nowhere to be seen. She must be upstairs in her cubicle beside the infirmary, unaware of what was going on; Sister Petra suffered from arthritis and was almost completely paralyzed. To drive the helpless old creature out into the world where she would be totally unable to fend for herself was of course insane. Still, she could not be left upstairs to be roasted alive, once the attackers lost patience and soaked the building with gasoline. In an instant Assunta's mind had been made up. She broke out of line and ran back upstairs.

Through broken windows stray bullets continued to whiz past her ears, but she pressed forward doggedly until she reached the hospital wing. The sick list had been negligible that week: two lay sisters who were ill with grippe, and a waif picked off the street for delousing and a milk cure prior to placement in the orphanage. But, as Assunta suspected, the old nun had been forgotten. She sat in her cubicle, untroubled as yet by the disturbance below. Weaving back and forth in her chair, Sister Petra toyed—her fingers were too stiff to count a paternoster—with her beads.

There was no time to lose with explanations. Assunta seized the old woman by both arms and pulled her forcibly into the hall.

Here the besiegers were apparently gaining ground, for the gunfire had grown louder and there were shouts coming up through the dark stair well. Were there any other exits? Assunta paused in confusion. More than once she had done infirmary duty, yet she felt momentarily trapped as though she had never been up here before.

Doubt began to assail her. Had she done right in bothering with the ailing crone whose existence had all but run its course? By now she, Assunta, might safely have reached the street in company with the other nuns, instead of risking two lives where only one had been endangered. After all, Sister Petra was not her personal responsibility. No one had ordered Assunta to run back into the threatened building on so quixotic a rescue mission.

No one?

She knew better than that. God's voice had spoken to her through the instrument of memory, as it may conceivably have spoken to others in the covey of fleeing nuns. Assunta alone seemed to have heard. Or, if the others heard, she alone had answered:

"Yes, poor miserable Sister Petra is upstairs. I will go back and fetch her——"

But where was she to turn now? Why did not God's voice speak again to help her remember the infirmary floor plan? The convent portals had been broken down and from the increasing rumble below it was plain that plundering had begun. There was no time to lose.

Fear clutched at Assunta's throat. To make matters worse, the old nun grasped the situation at last and broke into hysterical screams. Her strident cries were like nothing hu-

Capuchin Monastery in Vienna, containing Habsburg burial vaults.

Franz Josef in Austrian uniform under Schussnigg Regime.

man, for they bespoke the elemental reaction of the helpless, a blind, unthinking terror.

It was this outburst of witless fright which cleared Assunta's brain. Dragging the wailing woman behind her, she rushed back into the infirmary and headed straight for the linen room. Here, reason told her, must be the back stairs used by lay sisters to take away the weekly laundry.

She was right. Through a narrow door an unobstructed exit opened before them. With Sister Petra on her back, Assunta descended cautiously.

Downstairs she knew her way about. She had been assigned to altar duty through the Advent season, which entailed looking after the sacristy, the vestment room, as well as the candle, incense, and communion supplies. Here she was familiar with every nook and cranny. It would be a matter of seconds to rush Sister Petra into the shelter of the choir loft.

After reaching this temporary haven they could pause and catch their breath. Also, Assunta realized, they must plan their next move with particular foresight, as they had become separated from the remaining sisterhood and must fend for themselves as best they could.

Well, one thing was a blessing. Assunta had not been fooled by the outrageous togs foisted upon the other nuns. Being young, she remembered feminine fashions of two and three years ago; they were nothing like the pinch-waist, leg-o'-mutton garments into which the Mother Superior had allowed herself to be bamboozled. Instead, Assunta had quietly negotiated with the gardener's wife for some inconspicuous working clothes. Slender of build and broad-shouldered, she looked like hundreds of young Spanish girls who served in the guerrilla ranks of the Republic.

As a touch of further realism, Anselmo, the gardener, had

given her a Communist button with Lenin's picture imprinted across it. She was to pin this on her blouse and to hold up her right fist in salute whenever accosted by strangers.

The most immediate problem was of course Sister Petra who, blissfully unaware of coming perils, had made no preparation. She was still in full habit, with surplice, silver crucifix, veil, and a huge rosary dangling from her waist.

While figuring out what to do, Assunta hurriedly changed the old nun's appearance. Relieving Sister Petra of veil and coif, she bound Anselmo's bandanna over the cropped gray head. No one had thought of telling the invalid woman that she must let her hair grow, and it was doubtful in any case whether she could have raised any kind of thatch.

The next step presented something of a conundrum. How to alter the nun's somber habit from brown (a sure giveaway that she was a Teresiana) to some more innocuous shade? Assunta thought fast and reached a practical solution. For reasons of economy the nuns wore petticoats of a blue crash material which faded, through many washings, to a light slate shade. What could be simpler than to remove the dark overskirt and place it (for warmth) under the slip? As the latter ended in a flounce the effect was that of an ordinary peasant dress. To eliminate all further convent touches, the starched band of white must be ripped from Sister Petra's throat, and the silver chain and crucifix tucked inside her blouse. This accomplished, the old nun was ready.

She was exhausted from all the fussing about her pain-racked person. But now Assunta once more slung the helpless woman over her own back and headed for the outer passage. On steady feet she plodded through the Gaudi cloisters toward the vestibule beyond. At last she felt gravel underfoot and breathed the open air.

Her eyes blinked in the outside twilight that still reflected the sun's last rays blending into the fires above the town. There was a strange silence round about; the shouts and maledictions of the crowd seemed to have subsided. Where had the people gone? What had lured them away?

She could not know that, after capturing the Mother Superior and her little troupe of fugitives, the mob had believed the convent now empty and not worth further attention. Why waste time and petrol on a pile of stone? There were other conflagrations to be touched off—notably the halls of Bonanova, where many a Barcelona schoolboy had spent years of acute suffering. Yes, the hour of judgment had struck at last, even for Brother Saturnino!

Was there justice in such stark and indiscriminate retribution? The rabble did not analyze its own function as an instrument of punishment; it remained impersonal. When scourges visited the earth, as in Sodom, Pompeii, or plague-racked Asia, the saint died with the sinner. Ordeal by fire! The Spain of the Inquisition had risen again to cleanse itself of ancient wrongs. . . .

Dragging the nuns along, the frenzied populace had moved toward another part of town. Assunta and her companion were alone in the deserted street.

Through dust and smoke the last rays of day had vanished as Assunta staggered along twisted alleys toward the outskirts of the city. The woman on her back seemed to grow heavier with every step, yet she dared not pause for rest. They must find shelter for the night in some cave, or beside the frozen remains of a haystack in a field. Then there was the question of food. After bedding Sister Petra in some semblance of comfort, Assunta must forage for water and provisions.

Oddly, throughout all this she knew no fear. The deep, inner sense of performing a duty toward a fellow human being filled her with an abiding dignity and strength.

She had left Sister Petra leaning against a tree stump by the roadside, not far from a dimly lighted peasant cottage. The next step called for courage of a special sort. Raising her fist in the Communist salute, she must ask some passing stranger or near-by homesteader for help.

Boldly she knocked on the first cottage door, prepared to introduce herself as a guerrilla fighter. But at the last moment the realization that she carried no weapons caused her to drop the pose. A man appeared in the doorway, followed by a woman with a lantern. On the wall behind them Assunta discerned a cheap pottery statuette of the Infant Jesus of Prague, lighted by a stub of tallow. The sight of the humble image gave Assunta confidence.

"I have a companion," she said simply, "who fainted from weakness back there on the road. Can you give us some bread?"

Her forthrightness met with a kind response. The peasant couple noted the pallor of their visitor's face, despite the dust and grime that covered it. This was not the whiteness of fatigue, but that ashen color imparted by monastic living, shut off from wind and sun.

Assunta read the mute recognition in their eyes, as well as the assurance that no harm threatened here. She could drop her disguise and explain that she and Sister Petra were fugitive Teresianas in need of quick help.

The rest was easier than she had dared hope.

"Come in," urged the peasant wife, reaching out her hand. "Candelario will fetch the other one——"

With this she nudged her husband and handed him the lantern. He hurried noiselessly up the road where the old nun could be seen huddled against the tree.

For the rest of that night Assunta conferred with her hosts about the next step she must take. Candelario had a sister along the water front, whose husband was a fisherman. If Assunta could make her way there before dawn she might get aboard the fishing smack and be smuggled aboard some steamer out at sea. It was certainly worth trying.

"But Sister Petra," interposed the former Archduchess. "She is too ill to move any farther——"

The peasant wife made a reassuring gesture. "She can stay here until the danger passes. When she regains her strength we will see that she is taken to safety."

Assunta turned to Candelario. "How do you know your brother-in-law won't surrender me to the authorities?"

The peasant crossed himself and lowered his voice to a whisper. "He is a devout man. All this week he has been rescuing priests and nuns, putting them on ships headed for Rome."

"Rome?"

"Yes—have you not heard? The Holy Father promises shelter to all members of religious orders who manage to get out of Spain."

Here was solace indeed. With Sister Petra in good hands, Assunta decided to venture forth alone. She bade her benefactors farewell and set out that same night for the fishermen's wharf in Barceloneta.

Candelario's promise held good. The brother-in-law took Assunta on his barge and spirited her out beyond harbor limits, where an Italian liner lay at anchor.

A week later she had reached the Vatican, where a surprise awaited her. The Pope, it now developed, had certainly proclaimed his intention to look after his persecuted flock. But the growing number of refugees soon necessitated a modification of the original pledge, as there were not enough convents in Italy to receive the fugitive priests and nuns who poured in not only from Spain, but Germany and Russia as well. In addition, there were still the victims of earlier anti-clerical uprisings in Mexico to be disposed of. Obviously mankind faced a new era of religious intolerance. The Holy Father had his hands full.

In accord with his advisors, Pius XI reached a practical decision. All female members of religious orders who had no living relatives or means of support would be provided for within the hierarchy of the Church. But others who could boast even an eighth cousin with a roof over his head were automatically absolved of their vows and bidden to return into the world.

For Assunta this was a shocking blow. With all the passionate intensity of her nature she had given herself to God. Despite the incredulity of her kin she had provided ample proof of the sincerity of her vocation. She had weathered her novitiate and become a full-fledged nun. To be now forcibly relieved of her vows was a profound humiliation.

She protested before the clerical board that handled her case along with countless other suppliants who dreaded returning to a civilian life from which they had grown too long estranged. But it was no use. The Holy See could make no exceptions. Its monasteries and retreats were filled to capacity with jobless bishops, abbesses, and lesser dependents. An archduchess whose family still held title to the wineries of Viareggio could not properly be classed as indigent. Assunta's path was clearly indicated. She must go back to her own people.

It did not help that she had been out of touch with Mama

and the family for years. Where had they all been scattered?
Would she find anyone at Viareggio?

There was also the question of funds. On entering the
Order of the Teresianas, Assunta had been required to bring
a dowry and to pledge whatever inheritance fell to her on
her father's death. Today she was penniless. Needless to
say, since she returned to the world under duress, the
Church restored her cash.

Actually money meant nothing to her. What she grieved
for was the loss of her religious habit, her nun's cross, her
flowing veil. She would miss not only the solace of communal life within sanctified convent walls, but the very
trappings of monastic tradition. She felt actually homesick
for her lonely, whitewashed cell.

It was in a despondent mood that she arrived at Viareggio
where Ferrari, the major-domo, gave her a warm welcome.
He also handed her the keys to the cupboards of Tenuta
Reale, where she might find some suitable clothes.

Chapter Twenty-Six

LIKE HIS SISTER ASSUNTA, the Archduke Pepi was adrift in a none too friendly world.

After selling his Barcelona flying school and equipment, he had set out for Paris with high hopes. Apart from sufficient savings to tide him over uncertain times, he had one important factor in his favor. He had spent more than a decade in a Latin atmosphere, which lent him urbanity and, in Spanish and French, considerable eloquence. Proper application of these qualities soon won him his admission into the tourist promotion departments of the French and Dutch air lines. The pay was satisfactory, quite apart from promise of expansion and a glittering future.

The work entailed much travel, which on one occasion permitted Franz Josef to visit Mama in Vienna and to attend the baptism of Anton's and Ileana's son Stefan at Mödling.

During the short Austrian sojourn Franz Josef also paid his first call on the Kapuzinergruft, where his ancestors—and more recently Papa and Rainer—had been buried. In walking alone toward the Capuchin Church, he realized how little he really knew about the city of his birth. Having fled from Vienna as a small boy, the Austria of Strauss waltzes, Prater promenades, gay operettas by the glorious Franz Lehár, had a dreamlike, unreal quality. To him the notorious revelries at Sacher's and the garden spots of Hietzing were nothing but hearsay. He had never seen such landmarks as the Hofburgtheater, the Kathi Schratt house near Schönbrunn, or the interior of the single-spired Cathedral of Saint Stephen. Indeed, he scarcely remembered his own godfather, the patriarchal Emperor Franz Joseph I.

Wishing to call no attention either to his ignorance or to his identity, the Archduke Pepi bought a Baedeker from a newsstand. Book in hand, he next joined a party of Cook's tourists just entering the Capuchin Monastery under which lay the imperial tombs. A tonsured brother of the order admitted the visitors and with obvious practice assumed the role of guide.

The descent to the burial vaults was eerie and impressive, leading through dank passages into a region of shadows. Here slumbered history, as death itself gave testimony to the past.

To his surprise Franz Josef did not find the Kapuzinergruft a repugnant necropolis. Its various chambers, harboring emperors, kings, and princelets according to their chronology, presented a strangely vivid pageant of centuries gone by. There lay Maria Theresia, great sovereign of the Viennese rococo: her baroque coffin, encrusted with florid arabesques, evoked the sweet powdered-wig era of Mozart minuets and French pavanes. In another recess stood the Biedermeier sarcophagi of a more bourgeois Austria, touched here and there with parvenu Napoleonic elegance, as in the sepulture of the young Duke of Reichstadt. Lastly there was the ugly Second Baroque (given fullest rein in England's Victorian style) with all the grace and lightness replaced by pompous *chinoiserie*. Under its pretentious weight rested romantic Rudolph, he of the Mayerling tragedy, with his mother—Empress Elisabeth—close by. Then, lonely and austere, the casket of the soldierly monarch, Franz Joseph.

Yes, they were all there, except Franz Ferdinand and Sophie Chotek, victims of Sarajevo; and young Emperor Karl, sleeping on a mountain top in far Madeira.

For spectators who owned no Baedeker and were unversed in Habsburg lore, the Capuchin guide provided an unbroken pattern of statistical information. With a fluency gained by routine, he rattled off dates, names, and historic associations of each denizen in that vast crypt. Occasionally, for the benefit of practical-minded Americans, he shook silver locks and handles, with the one-word comment:

"Sterling!"

Once or twice he also lifted his cassock and gave one of the coffins a resounding kick.

"Solid copper," he divulged matter-of-factly.

In moving from chamber to chamber the monk added a few gratuitous remarks concerning the cost of keeping up the vaults, now that they had become state property and the imperial family no longer was permitted to pay for their care. Experienced tourists recognized this prelude to the passing of the collection plate. Without grumbling, they reached into their pockets.

Though no one knew his identity, Franz Josef felt a tinge of embarrassment on discovering that his dead kin continued to do business from the Great Beyond. While coins tinkled briskly into the collection platter, he stepped back through the arch of the Toscana vault, where stood the biers of his recently deceased father and brother. He observed that the built-in flower holders contained fresh blooms. Mama must be a frequent visitor here.

While he lingered, wrapped in meditation, there was a sudden thunderous clap followed by equally sudden darkness. It took him several seconds to realize that the little band of sight-seers must have departed and the door to the vault had clanged shut. The Capuchin friar, finished with his task, was dousing the lights. He did so by means of an outside switch.

For a moment Franz Josef was stupefied with shock. Then, feeling his way through the pitch-black gloom, he fumbled about until he reached the door, only to find his worst suspicion verified. It was locked. He pounded on the heavy panel, first with his fists, then by resorting to vigorous kicks (such as had been administered to the coffins only a short while earlier). But there was no response. Either the door panels were too thick for sound to carry through, or else the monks upstairs—if they heard any subterranean noises—took them to be the work of some unholy phantom. It occurred to Franz Josef that the Capuchin brethren might well be conscience-stricken about that matter of the collection plate. If so, they doubtlessly were busy crossing themselves right now and sending up prayers for the exorcism of angered Habsburg demons who might be launching protests from the grave. In any case, there was not the slightest indication that anyone upstairs intended to come to Franz Josef's rescue.

He paused in the darkness. And now a feeling of being utterly forsaken—yet somehow engulfed by a vast pulsating presence—overcame him. He was alone with his ancestors. Round about him the very air seemed to contain in intensified measure the essence of generations and centuries of living. There was nothing macabre about this strange sensation, just as there had been nothing macabre about that gaudy, romantic Habsburg world which lay buried here. Even in its hours of starkest melodrama—Maximilian's fiasco in Mexico, Empress Elisabeth's assassination at Geneva (the city of peace!), Mayerling, Sarajevo—the dynasty retained a warm and thrilling hold upon the imagination. They had not been tyrants, maniacs, or murderers, these dead who lay here beside the matriarch Maria Theresia. Their faults had leaned in the direction of too much humanity: great lovers they had been, spendthrift cavaliers, easygoing statesmen. In death there was about them yet the memory of bell-clear Mozart music and the sweep of a magnificent lost waltz. . . .

Franz Josef stood and listened. He heard all this as a stranger might hear. For he was a stranger here among his own people. He was a Habsburg who had grown to manhood far removed from the compelling spell of the Habsburg legend.

His reveries were interrupted now by an involuntary shudder that ran down his spine. The crypt, shut off from the fresh current of sun-warmed air admitted during the tourist inspection, was returning to its former sepulchral chill. The very atmosphere seemed to congeal within this sunken world of still, white marble.

Fear gripped him suddenly. Was he going to be left here through the waning afternoon and (ghastly thought!) the night? Would no one come to unlock the vault before morning, when the next batch of sight-seers turned up?

A second worry seized him. What if tomorrow there happened to be no tourists?

This frightful possibility recalled to him his own job as promotion manager for French and Dutch travel interests. He wondered what kind of setup existed in Vienna; was there a go-getting agent, capable of whipping up trade? If not, Heaven help the Archduke Pepi! With Austrian tourist advertising in improper hands, days might go by— even a week—before another foreign visitor appeared. Which brought him straight back to his present plight. He had left no word with anyone as to his whereabouts, since the pilgrimage to the Kapuziner had occurred to him on the spur of the moment. If he were missed, no one would have the faintest idea where to look for him. Mama, Dolores and Carlos were not pedantic about time schedules; if he did not show up they would suppose a pressing business obligation had forced him to rush to the airport and board a plane for France.

"He will wire," they would say philosophically. Morbid worrying had never been a family trait.

As for Franz Josef, he felt far from philosophical just now. Envisioning a week of Stygian darkness, hunger and thirst, he knew there could be only one outcome. For once the Habsburg clan would be saved funeral expenses, as he was certain to perish right on the spot where he belonged. No need for exequies, processions, or pomp for an archduke who had already reached his destination; Fate would simplify matters by causing him to "join" his ancestors not only metaphorically but in fact.

He found the prospect depressing. True, all men must ultimately keep their rendezvous with Death, but this was rushing it a bit. Surely there was a way to postpone the unwelcome appointment.

Perhaps he ought to pray?

That was it: he would entreat the heavens to send just one more caravan of Cook's customers before dusk. He must direct his tourist propaganda straight to God.

It worked.

Within forty-five minutes (which seemed like so many hours) after the departure of the last visitors there was a sound of footsteps above. A moment later Franz Josef recognized an unmistakable metallic clang: the comforting rattle of a bunch of keys. The door to the vault moaned on its hinges, admitting a fresh troupe of tittering and excited visitors. At sight of them Franz Josef bounded from the shadows in one frantic leap.

The effect of his sudden appearance out of the crypt's silent depths proved almost disastrous. The terrified sightseers broke into shrieks of horror, mistaking the tall—and very pale—Habsburg for a wraith. Two ladies fainted, while the Capuchin guide himself gave evidence of funk as he shrank back to a respectful distance.

But the Archduke Pepi was far too relieved at his own escape from the nether regions to indulge in ghostly pranks on his rescuers. This was no time for diablerie. Grinning ingratiatingly from ear to ear, he bowed and introduced himself, adding profuse assurance of his imperial gratitude.

It took some grinning and bowing, as the chary spectators harbored some doubts. But once they became convinced that the apparition was indeed flesh and blood, there were general expressions of delight. To think of a routine inspection of the Kapuzinergruft with a live Habsburg thrown in for good measure! The customers of Thomas Cook and Company had certainly got more than their money's worth.

The collection plate jangled agreeably that day.

Chapter Twenty-Seven

FOLLOWING THIS HARROWING EXPERIENCE, Franz Josef wound up his Vienna visit in haste. He headed for Holland by way of Germany, making a survey of tourist propaganda en route. It was during a short stopover in Berlin that Fate singled him out for another blow, this time straight to the heart.

Through a friend by the extraordinary name of Pons Dunkelsbuehler he heard a melancholy tale concerning a young woman, greatly admired by Pons, who lay on her deathbed.

"What is her name?" Franz Josef asked, as yet not very moved.

"Marta-Vienna," said Dunkelsbuehler with a sigh.

"Marta-Vienna? But that's absurd; nobody could have a name like that!"

Pons emerged from his grief long enough to make an explanation. "Her real name is Marta Aloyse Bäumer; now divorced Baroness von Kahler; her father was an army officer and her mother a Countess Locatelli. But she is herself the loveliest thing that ever came out of Austria, and so everyone calls her Marta-Vienna."

"I see," said Franz Josef, still undisturbed. "What is her illness?"

"A strange fever, diagnosed as incurable. She is going to die——"

"How can you be sure?"

"She is wasting away," lamented Pons. "I can't stand it. I break down when I see her. But still I go, because she

245

mustn't be alone. She hates living in Germany. She is homesick for Austria!"

It was his friend's anguish which touched the Archduke. He had always been an easy mark for the suffering and the distressed. Besides, was he not recently recovered from a whole year's weeping for a dead love? Dunkelsbuehler's grief was really his meat; nothing appealed to Franz Josef more strongly than the Camille theme, with himself in the role of an eternal Armand. His favorite operas were *La Traviata* and *La Bohème,* wherein the note of pity rose over every other passion.

He turned to his friend. "What can I do?"

"Go to her in my place," pleaded Pons. "Just once, until I pull myself together——"

By this time the Archduke Pepi's curiosity had been aroused. He began to feel himself drawn irresistibly to his friend's ailing protégée.

"Will she receive me?" he asked.

"I'll telephone the nurse," replied Pons, full of solicitude. "They will expect you. Here is the address——"

It was thus that Franz Josef set out on his somewhat unconventional mission of mercy. Purchasing an armload of flowers and a box of chocolates (hardly recommended for a lady *in extremis*), he hastened to pay a sympathetic call.

He found the Baroness bedded on a couch in a heavily shaded sitting room that opened on her boudoir.

"She insisted on being carried out here," whispered the attending nurse. "She wanted to receive Your Imperial Highness in as fitting a fashion as possible."

He was moved by this small gesture of homage. The dynasty had not of late been spoiled with favors. It pleased him to find the unknown lady not only an ardent Austrian, but seemingly well disposed toward the fallen monarchy.

Franz Josef on tiger hunt in India.

Fishing in Florida.

Left: Archduchess (former nun) Assunta at home of her sister-in-law.

Beyond these minor conjectures there was not much he could learn about Pons Dunkelsbuehler's dying friend, for she was too ill to talk at any length, and in the dimness of the room it was almost impossible to make out her face. If she was indeed a famous beauty he had so far seen no proof.

That night over assorted beakers of wine, he and Pons discussed the situation.

"She is very sick," the Archduke confirmed Dunkelsbuehler's opinion. "I think I ought to go again——"

Pons readily agreed. He was fast reaching a state of nervous prostration. Franz Josef's offer brought him untold relief, as he could let himself go and work up to a paroxysm of picturesque pain.

On the occasion of the Archduke's second visit the Baroness lay again upon her couch, as she was to do during the weeks that followed. Soon Franz Josef's appearances had become a daily occurrence, together with the flowers and the obligatory candy, the latter being eaten by the nurse, a housemaid, and himself. As time went by he fell prey to an intense and not altogether selfless emotion. He still did not know what the Baroness looked like, but it became daily clearer that he was falling in love with her.

He told Dunkelsbuehler.

"Oh, that isn't surprising," was the latter's answer. "I told you she is wonderful!"

"But—I mean——" Franz Josef was at a loss for words.

Pons cut him short by launching ecstatically into a brief sketch of the Baroness von Kahler's biography.

"She is well born, as I told you. But under family pressure she was married—very young, you understand—to a rich Czechoslovakian sugar exporter."

"Baron von Kahler?"

"Yes. He had a castle—Zvinař—near Prague, and a villa in Hamburg. He took his wife to Hamburg."

"What happened then?"

"Oh, the inevitable. Her lively Viennese temperament was unsuited to her husband's sterner ways, quite apart from the mental depression any southerner would suffer under the vile Hamburg climate."

"Of course," nodded Franz Josef, his heart swelling with emotion.

"She had a house full of servants," continued Pons, "yet she was always alone. Hamburg is a *Patrizierstadt,* a city of extreme formality, where people are hard to know and to make friends with."

The Archduke Pepi could not bear it. His mood called for Chopin music played by his Spanish friend, Nicolás Casina, who for a while had helped Franz Josef mourn a lost Chilean love.

"What did she do?" he wanted to know. "The Baroness, I mean——"

"She ordered the gloomy Hamburg mansion refurnished in Viennese baroque, with Aubusson rugs, jolly porcelain heating stoves in every room, and gay bright mirrors. She also bought gramophone records of every known *csárdás* and waltz. And then do you know what she did?"

"No, what?"

"She called her German servants into the parlor and taught them to dance in three-quarter time! What, my friend, do you think of that?"

Pons beamed his own answer to a purely rhetorical question. It proved an unnecessary answer since his listener agreed. In fact, the Archduke Franz Josef was entranced. "How utterly charming!"

"Baron von Kahler did not think so. The marriage, as you see, went on the rocks."

There was now no checking the Archduke's infatuation. Throwing his arm about Dunkelsbuehler's shoulder, he cried ecstatically:

"You are right—she is wonderful!"

"Yes," Pons nodded gloomily. "And isn't it too bad——? Because she is dying——"

They brooded awhile longer over their cups and then Franz Josef went back to hold the death watch.

Oddly, from this point on matters took an unexpected turn. In the face of the most pessimistic medical prognostications the doomed Baroness began showing signs of improvement. After hovering for weeks on the brink of eternity, she rallied and began to gain in strength.

This led to a new conference between the Archduke and his friend. The long strain had begun to tell on Pons, until he himself was ready to take to his bed. Having keyed his mind to funereal thoughts for better than a month, he could not weather the sudden and wondrous change.

"Please keep going to her," he implored his partner in the three-cornered romance. "It may be only a sham improvement before the end. . . . If so, I couldn't face it——"

Franz Josef did not hold the waning illness to be sham. He was concerned now about another matter. Up to this moment his love for the mysterious patient had been fed by the poignant element of impending tragedy. Not long for this world, according to considered medical judgment, the Baroness had symbolized for him the Unattainable, a Fata Morgana, a chimeric dream. The realization that she would recover called for readjustment on his part. It was one thing to worship an illusion, and quite another to be threatened with its taking form.

Speaking of form, he found himself of late thinking in concrete terms. His ideal of beauty had changed since the days of his sultry and brunette Chilean amour. He now liked blondes, but they must be willowy and tall. He wondered whether the Baroness, once she was on her feet and he really got a look at her, would measure up.

This preoccupation troubled Franz Josef a great deal more than did the superfluous Dunkelsbuehler. After all, the gentle Pons was too noble a character to thwart the course of true love; he would surrender the field. But what would happen to Franz Josef's love if, once the curtains were thrust aside and daylight flooded the sickroom, Marta-Vienna revealed herself as dark and dumpy? The thought was agonizing.

Fortunately all this came under the heading of gratuitous worry, as the Archduke had a surprise coming. Timing her convalescence to proper advantage, the sick lady shunned exposure till the ravages of her ordeal had been all but obliterated. Only when she felt certain of her charm was the veil of secrecy lifted, so that Franz Josef might behold her at her radiant best.

He remained breathless.

She was everything he had dreamed of, and more. Regally tall and fair, she had something besides extraordinary beauty: an unquestionable poise and style. In addition she possessed the warmth and wit and readiness for laughter of the born Viennese. From death's door she had returned, resilient, joyous, indestructible. For, as he was to learn in years to come, she had enormous physical stamina and spiritual strength.

But there was yet another quality that drew him to her irretrievably. This was an intangible power that sprang deep from her Danube roots. It embodied the thing he had lacked most of his life as, moving about in exile, he had been dogged by the cognizance of his own homelessness. Here in this one woman was all the best of Austria, for she was Austria itself. Everything that he had missed—and longed for hopelessly—was crystallized in her exuberant person. No longer would he be plagued by the echo of a lost waltz which he had never really heard. To Marta it was not lost, for she had danced it. She would teach it to him as she had taught her Hamburg servants. She would help him to find himself. Marta was *Home*.

Things happened quickly from now on. Having made up his mind that he could not endure life without her, Franz Josef proposed.

He was not immediately accepted. Marta knew better than he the obstacles that would be thrown in the path of a Habsburg bent on contracting a *mésalliance*. The monarchy had fallen, but there was still a rigorous dynastic code to be observed. More specifically, there lived at Steenockerzeel in Belgium the Empress Zita and her son Otto, highest arbiters of conduct for all members of the imperial house. Franz Josef would need their approval before carrying out his marriage plans.

He did not really think so, but on Marta's insistence he set out for Steenockerzeel. The trip irked him. Having lived too far removed from formalism, he rebelled against the snobbery of class distinctions. Royal matches, as contrived by all the dynasties of Europe (including "democratic" England), were an anachronism and a farce. Times were changing. In a truly modern world men and women met on equal terms, regardless of accidental wealth or title.

Franz Josef was not alone in holding this opinion. His father had held it before him. As far back as 1922, after the death of the Emperor Karl, the Archduke Leopold Salvator had made a motion to revise the Habsburg marriage laws. For this purpose he had journeyed especially to Switzerland where the late Emperor's brother, Maximilian (Archduke Max), lived in exile. Until Otto's majority, Maximilian acted as head of the scattered imperial household.

In submitting his proposal Papa had come prepared with lucid arguments. For one thing, he pointed out, the marriage laws were both obsolete and flagrantly unjust, as they had been set up centuries ago by a chief of protocol whose bumptious pride was equaled only by his ignorance.

"This imbecile," sputtered Leopold Salvator, "devised an arbitrary list of sixteen ruling houses among which a Habsburg might choose a mate. In his abysmal stupidity he included only such names as he could personally remember, leaving out—among others—all the Grandees of Spain, who by decree are cousins to the King!"

Maximilian listened without enthusiasm. He had himself shown eminent taste in wedding one of the sixteen acceptable names: Princess Francisca zu Hohenlohe-Waldenburg-Schillingsfürst von Ratibor und Corvey. His descendants, up to the current generation at least, suffered no proletarian taint.

Leopold Salvator thereupon invited him to look at the problem from a more practical angle.

"It will soon be a question of pure arithmetic," he argued patiently. "There are bad days ahead for royalty and even lesser aristocrats. The blue bloods are thinning out. If we don't let down the bars our children may soon have a hard time marrying anyone at all!"

Clearly these were the words of a devoted father of a family of ten. The Archduke Max listened with only mild sympathy.

"The law has existed a long time," he remarked sententiously. "It is not for us to tamper with accepted custom."

If Papa had felt less earnestly about the matter he might have been amused. His retort was almost a taunt:

"Since when is something good just because it happens to be old? Do mistakes grow venerable with the years?"

But Maximilian was in no mood for debate. The marriage regulations, he said quietly, would not be relaxed. Leopold Salvator realized that his mission was hopeless.

He returned to Barcelona with a firm decision which he promptly passed on to his children: "You are free to make your own laws. I want you to marry anyone you wish!"

Despite this generous paternal gesture Franz Josef was still in awe of family tradition. He resolved to seek an audience at Steenockerzeel where the indomitable Zita held sway. Either through the Empress or the young Pretender, Otto, he planned to succeed where his father had failed.

Needless to say, his hopes were none too high. Under a stern mother's tutelage Otto had grown up in an atmosphere of disciplined austerity. It was not likely that he would undertake to loosen the dynastic apron strings.

Franz Josef's guess proved correct. Like Uncle Max before him, Otto remained unreceptive to any idea of streamlining the family statutes. For a moment the Archduke Pepi felt tempted to remark caustically that this might well be the reason Zita and her children were no longer welcome in the new Austria. But he swallowed his rancor and made a courteous exit.

As for the Baroness von Kahler, he came to a quick decision. They would marry without permission. Dynastic pride? Fiddlesticks! Franz Josef was a simple breadwinner, self-supporting and independent from the imperial cash drawer. No government paid him an allowance, and so he needed no official sanction in so personal a matter as the choice of a wife.

In marrying him, Marta would not be recognized by Habsburg family code as an imperial archduchess. But the Schuschnigg Republic, having reinstituted properties and titles, made no distinction between man and wife. Also, there was the unprejudiced attitude of Hungary: the Magyars, monarchists for a thousand years, nevertheless attached no stigma to morganatic marriages. At Budapest the bride of Franz Josef would be hailed as his equal in every regard.

Happy in this realization, he went ahead with his plans. Immediately on leaving Steenockerzeel he wrote a letter to his mother, asking her blessing and approval. He also requested permission to place in Marta's hands a prized family jewel, the brooch of Marie Antoinette, which had come down to the Infanta through the Bourbon line.

Needless to say, Mama replied in a hearty affirmative, for she shared her late husband's liberal opinions. With thrones toppling everywhere, it was meaningless for royal children to continue sacrificing themselves on the altar of political expediency. Since their countries had nothing to gain or lose by dynastic matchmaking, let them have the commoner's supreme privilege of marrying for love. . . .

Chapter Twenty-Eight

FROM STEENOCKERZEEL the Archduke Franz Josef did not return to Berlin. Political events were moving fast at that time and his presence on German soil would have been fraught with danger. For Hitler had moved, on March 11, 1938, into Austria. Under the terms of the Anschluss all Habsburgs were technically under arrest.

In Vienna the Infanta Blanca found herself suddenly under guard and confined to her premises because she refused to obey the first order issued by the occupation forces, namely to raise a Nazi flag. Together with the oldest and youngest of her children, Dolores and Carlos, she remained locked in the small apartment assigned her at the Palais Toscana, in the Fourth District, Argentinierstrasse 29, while a giant swastika was nailed above her door. Food and news of the outside world were brought to the captives by the faithful Stepanek and the pianist Edgar Schiffmann, who had been sponsored by the Infanta at frequent Red Cross concerts during the Great War.

Anton and Ileana faced similar restrictions at their country home, Schloss Sonnberg near Hollabrunn, fifty kilometers from Vienna. With their children, Stefan, Minola, and Alexandra (a fourth, Dominik, was to be born in July of that year), they sat out the storm in relative safety. Hitler did not want trouble with Ileana's homeland, Romania, and so the Habsburgs at Hollabrunn remained under supervision but otherwise unmolested.

It was for a similar reason that the Infanta Blanca suffered no actual hardship beyond restriction of her freedom. Though Spain had currently no use for any member of its royal house, public opinion in Madrid would have censured any act of violence committed abroad against the dethroned dynasty. Her Spanish blood rendered the Infanta immune.

This advantage did not apply to other Habsburgs, notably the sons of Archduke Franz Ferdinand and Sophie Chotek. Bearing their mother's morganatic title of Hohenberg, the two brothers Maximilian and Ernst, respectively thirty-four and thirty-two years old, had been signaled as enemies of the new order and taken to the notorious concentration camp of Dachau in Bavaria. The fact that Ernst had a British wife (née Mary Wood), while Maximilian left five small sons behind, did not mitigate their lot. The two princes were assigned to a labor battalion where they faced greater hardships than the camp's Jews. They worked in stone quarries, shoveled manure, pushed heavy wheelbarrows, emptied the camp slops, and cleaned the latrines.

The same fate would have been in store for Archduke Felix, brother of the Pretender Otto, had he not made his escape in time. Felix had been attending a Vienna school when rumors of the impending Anschluss caused him to skip across the border into Czechoslovakia. To effect his extradition by Prague authorities, the charge was made that he had stolen silver plate from the school's dining room. So absurd was this trumped-up accusation that even the anti-Habsburg Eduard Beneš allowed the twenty-year-old lad to go on his way unhampered.

As for Otto himself, a pronouncement was issued from Berlin, placing a price on his head. This, and the fact that underground reports pointed to a new world war in the offing, caused the Steenockerzeel household to plan another hegira. The Empress Zita and her children were once more on the move.

Franz Josef for his part had also arrived at a quick choice.

As Marta had meanwhile preceded him to England, he crossed the Channel and joined her there as quickly as possible. They were married under British law. Due to the bridegroom's Spanish citizenship, they signed the register as Prince and Princess Francisco José de Habsburg-Borbón (Bourbon), which would be the correct names thenceforth used on their passports.

The occasion drew no headlines or official comment. A London columnist, however, permitted himself the observation that the handsome bride looked "the way an archduchess *ought* to look, but never does. . . . "

There was no question of a honeymoon trip, both for economic reasons and because of the precarious political situation prevailing throughout Europe. The former Baroness von Kahler was wealthy in her own right, but she had not been able to transfer her income to England. On the other hand, even if this feat had been accomplished, it would have been difficult to think of a place to go. The powder keg of Europe was once more on the verge of blowing up.

At precisely this point Franz Josef ran head-on into a stroke of luck. Still actively engaged in his tourist promotion job, he had made contact with British travel agencies in the hope of spreading his efforts over other (and safer) continents. His one dream was to come to America. But Asia claimed him first. Or rather, the Maharaja of Rajpipla, from the Rewa Kantha hill country beyond Bombay.

The Maharaja happened to be visiting London, where he became entranced with Western fashions, sports, culture, and plumbing. He longed to introduce these benefits to his tiny principality (an area of 1,517 square miles) along the banks of the rivers Nerbudda and Tapti. He also wished to attract tourists to Rajpipla inasmuch as the state coffers could do with a new source of revenue.

The latter question brought him into contact with the publicity-minded Archduke. Having seen some of Franz Josef's displays and propaganda leaflets in Holland and France, the Maharaja besought the Cook offices to facilitate a meeting. The rest was child's play. Without the faintest notion of Indian geography in general, or the toy kingdom of Rajpipla in particular, the Archduke Pepi enthusiastically agreed to aid the progress-minded potentate. Though he had never even heard the name before, he promised to put the Maharaja's capital of Nandod (by the river Karjan) on the map.

"I shall need some time, however," he added candidly, "to study up on Rajpipla. Do you know any good books?"

The Maharaja was afraid he didn't. But he had an idea. "Why not come with me to my palace in Nandod, where you can learn about Rajpipla firsthand? While you are there you can build me an airport."

It was a capital suggestion. Franz Josef accepted with alacrity. Here was the wedding trip he and Marta had not dared to hope for.

Under the Maharaja's aegis, arrangements were promptly made, with the archducal pair prominently listed amid the oriental retinue. The voyage was made on a liner of the P & O Mail Packet Co., with ideal cruising weather and every conceivable comfort. For Franz Josef the experience became a revelation. He had been too small at the time of Austria's collapse to retain more than a hazy picture of imperial splendors. The luxury surrounding an Asiatic prince impressed him beyond measure.

"This is a gentleman's life!" he observed appreciatively.

At Rajpipla he was to gasp with even greater wonderment. The miniature realm of scarcely 90,000 souls (frequently decimated by periods of famine) kept its ruling house in

The Gardener's Cottage in Tarrytown during alterations.

Archduke Franz Josef during remodeling of cottage in
Tarrytown-on-Hudson.

fairy-tale opulence, for the Maharaja was a scion of the line of Bhaunagar, believed endowed with divinity. He enjoyed the lordly title of Gohel Rajput and was addressed as Thakor Sahib. A kindly liege, he was revered by Moslem and Hindu alike.

The palace of Nandod lay on the fringe of jungle territory, some thirty miles from Surat. It was not large, but incredibly lavish in all its appointments, like a vision out of the Arabian Nights sprung suddenly to life. Here, Franz Josef realized, one moved no longer as a mere gentleman. To his people the Maharaja was a demigod.

He was not a demigod, however, to the dynasty of the neighboring state of Baroda. The reason for this went back more than a generation. Since ancient times the feudal princes of Baroda—descendants of the fierce Kshatriyas of Mahratta—had terrorized weaker tribes and carried devastation across their borders. By repeated aggression they had enlarged their territories until Baroda became the dominant state in the region. Its ruler, the Gaekwar, exacted tribute from every town and village within a radius of two hundred miles. He got it, too—from everyone except the stubborn little anthill of Rajpipla. Surrounded by dangerous jungle, and protected by the natural barrier of three crocodile-infested rivers, Rajpipleans were a testy lot.

"If you want money," they said in effect, "come and get it!"

In 1873 the then Gaekwar of Baroda, a despot named Malhar Rao, took up the challenge and marched on tiny Nandod. But Rajpipla was ready for him. From hidden guerrilla nests posted in thicket and swampland, the invaders were given so savage a welcome that they stumbled head first into the Karjan River. Thousands were drowned and devoured by the waiting monsters below, while the remainder—in full rout—scrambled up the opposite bank. Among these latter was the very chagrined Gaekwar.

He had scarcely time, however, to express either astonishment or anger, for the maddened Rajpipleans were hard on his heels, chasing him across the borders of his own realm. It was a terrific race, ending only within sight of Malhar Rao's capital. But what lifted the incident into the sphere of hallowed legend was the fact that the Gaekwar had been obliged to run so fast that he lost his shoes. They were carried back in triumph to Nandod, where they occupied thenceforth a place of prominence in Rajpipla's shrine of war trophies. As for the aftermath to the battle, an interesting tradition took form. A lasting peace treaty was signed between Baroda and Rajpipla; but any descendants of Malhar Rao who wished to cross the river Karjan for a friendly call must leave their shoes at home. It was Rajpipla's intention never to let Baroda forget her barefoot Gaekwar. . . .

These and other facts were absorbed by the Archduke Franz Josef for the purpose of opening the Maharaja's storied land to travel-hungry tourists. Adept at aerial photography, he took innumerable pictures, catching the exotic beauty of that Asiatic world. But to complete the canvas, the Maharaja added a climax of his own. He arranged a tiger hunt.

The preparations were elaborate in the extreme, as the chase was in India a princely sport. Clothes, boots, topees, and other equipment were provided by the wardrobe master, while the Maharaja himself supervised the distribution of ammunition and guns. The party set out in motor caravans to the edge of the jungle, to continue from there—safari fashion—on foot.

There were no actual shooting boxes, such as European

hunters employed. Instead, great clumps of thicket and brush had been reinforced by staves and a bit of hemp rope, to afford temporary hideouts along the stalking route. As these "shelters" were flimsy and improvised at best, good aim was required of the hunter, once his prey came into view. A beast that was slightly wounded or merely startled by a poor shot could leap into the makeshift cover and tear its occupants to pieces.

In the distribution of the hunting party the Austrian guests remained at the Maharaja's side. According to etiquette, the Gohel Rajput or Great Lord must be the first to pull the trigger. If his aim proved faulty it might well be that the hunt ended right then and there, with a Thakor Sahib instead of a tiger in the bag; this was a chance any guest must take with so gallant a host.

The Archduke and his bride took it, very nearly to their eternal regret. For, as the zero hour approached and a magnificent Bengal tiger padded softly within range, the Maharaja's gun popped off with a huge clatter—and missed. The proud animal stood still and measured his surroundings with flaming eyes. Then, catching the scent of his human attacker, he reared and sprang high into the air. It was at this point that Franz Josef decided to do without etiquette. Shouldering his gun, he let go a blast at the beast's white belly. The tiger seemed to coil like a giant boa in midair, then fell sprawling at the Maharaja's feet.

That night a banquet was spread outdoors near the edge of the palace grounds. While nameless dishes, rich in spices and rare condiments, were passed around, the Habsburg guests drank in the mystic beauty of an Asiatic sky. But there was rivalry on the ground for the glittering constellations above. Aside from the lighted braziers, where servants kept the food at blistering temperature, there was a circle of glowing orbs that pierced the darkness.

"It's like a chain made out of balls of fire," exclaimed Marta, rising to inspect the marvel at closer range.

The Maharaja raised a restraining hand.

"The view is better from here," he admonished. "Those gleaming things you see are the eyes of jackals that creep through the town at night, sometimes to the very steps of the palace."

The archducal couple gave a little gasp. A dead tiger, a Lucullan banquet eaten off the ground, an anecdote concerning a Gaekwar who had lost his shoes—all this they had taken in their stride. But to sit for hours under the leering gaze of a solid ring of jackals! It was too much. A trifle shaky about the knees, the European visitors begged to be shown to their rooms.

There was a great deal more to Rajpipla, mused Franz Josef, than could possibly go into any tourist folder.

Chapter Twenty-Nine

THE ORIENTAL SOJOURN extended over six exciting weeks. During this time Rajpipla gained an airport laid out after the most modern specifications, as well as a flying school in which Franz Josef served as pioneer instructor. Since he was also a glider pilot, the manipulation of motorless craft was likewise included in the course. In short, the Maharaja's dream had been realized. Rajpipla could take its place among the world's up-to-date countries.

Their Asiatic mission accomplished, the Archduke and his bride returned to France. During the long and leisurely voyage back they found time to scale down their briefly acquired habits of luxury: life in Europe would not be the same as under a Maharaja's roof.

Even so, Franz Josef was eager to get back into the world of business. He enjoyed work. Throughout the Asiatic visit, during which he had directed the labors of others rather than carrying them out in person, he had studied India's attitude toward manual occupation. At Nandod and in the neighbor realm of Baroda all work done by hands was considered an indignity; only pariahs would stoop to touch the plow. Everywhere in India there prevailed a marked preference for pastoral over agricultural pursuits, an attitude which Franz Josef remembered also from rural Spain, and which characterized nomadic gypsy races all over the world. There existed a large branch of the human family that would not bow its head, like the working ox, under a yoke: to such peoples the shepherd or the herdsman stood far above the farmer. Their attitude moreover was supported by the caprice of Nature, notoriously unmerciful toward the tiller of the soil. After a year's sweat and sacrifice, the farmer more often than not faced devastation and famine. The shepherd, doing nothing, always had his flock; therefore he was a lord among men.

Well, it was no use carrying back such charming and seignorial notions to a Europe that would soon be plagued with vastly different problems. On the heels of its next ruinous war the white man's world (and woman's) was due for a long era of plain grubbing. No Rajputs here; only the dawn of proletarianism on a universal scale. Franz Josef intended to prepare for it. The one thing he did not fear was honest work.

On reaching French soil he surveyed the tourist situation, which was still fair, though Air France had slashed its advertising budget for the coming year. This was due only in part to the fear of war, but more particularly to the impending New York World's Fair, which would draw travelers *to* rather than *from* America.

America! There it was again—the Mecca of Franz Josef's dreams. If only he could find a way of getting there!

A trifling circumstance came to his rescue. In a column of the Paris *Herald* he read that Grover Whalen was currently in Europe, summering at Deauville. There ought to be no difficulty in making this important man's acquaintance.

Packing a pair of bags, the archducal couple dashed to the fashionable resort. Here another unexpected eventuality favored them in an almost prearranged manner. It was a lover's quarrel at the hotel where Franz Josef and Marta took lodgings. The assistant manager of the place had for some time been courting a lady of considerable ambition and pulchritude. As she was also a social climber he searched tirelessly for occasions to place her in the lime-light.

That season, under the mayor's benevolent sponsorship, Deauville planned to hold a combination fashion and dog show to be entitled *"La Belle et la Bête."* Monsieur Piquot, the assistant manager, was enthralled. Promptly he enrolled his adored Mademoiselle Suzy as a contestant. But he had neglected to study the exact terms of the event, namely that each competing lady must lead a canine candidate on a leash as she paraded along a special boardwalk set up on the beach. Picking names at random, the contest judges had in fact paired off Mademoiselle Suzy with a handsome Afghan hound named Gogo, entered by a local dog fancier.

As this fact dawned upon the damsel in question, she made a scene which was no storm in a teacup. With shouts of rage and colorful imprecations she gave out large pieces of her mind. Complete in public with—in French—a lousy pooch? Not she! Let other contestants stoop to such con-nivance. She needed no four-legged help to add up winning points.

This left Monsieur Piquot on the horns of a dilemma, admittedly an uncomfortable position. What to do? All announcements and newspaper publicity had made mention of the combination pet and fashion show. Deauville beauty parlors were doing a record business as poodles and schnauz-ers came to be groomed alongside their doting owners. To change plans now might provoke a minor riot, besides of-fending Gogo.

Here was the crux of the situation. The hotel manager would make Monsieur Piquot responsible not only for up-setting the whole program, but for administering a snub to the exquisitely shampooed Afghan and his owner.

Sadly Monsieur Piquot turned to his lady love. "I don't want to hurt Gogo," he said.

She stamped her dainty feet. "Either the dog is out of the picture or I am——"

"You are," replied Monsieur Piquot, choosing between *l'amour* and a good job.

This still left the problem unsolved. With the enraged young woman eliminated from the contest, who would lead Gogo in the parade?

It was at this precise moment that the Archduke Franz Josef and his bride breezed into Deauville. At sight of the magnificently blonde Marta, the worried committee relaxed. Here was a prize winner if ever they had seen one. But how to win this lovely woman to the cause?

Well, after all, had not Monsieur Piquot upset the apple-cart? Let him right it again!

The assistant manager was a shy but upright character. Without embellishing the facts, he introduced himself and presented his case, imploring Marta to take part and save the imperiled show.

She thought the story vastly amusing. Walk with a dog along a beach? But certainly! Why not? She was as free from false pride as she was truly beautiful. It did not ruffle her in the least to step into the breach as a replacement. She felt no pang at being second choice.

As for the parade of "Beauty and the Beast," it ended in a resounding success, with Marta and Gogo winning first prize. This consisted of an engraved silver cup and a dress designed by a leading Paris firm, whose Deauville representative was already on hand to take measurements. For Marta it was all a great lark. Cheerfully she surrendered the cup to the barking Afghan, and posed for the dressmaker. There was no woman alive who could not do with a new gown. . . .

There were many notables among the spectators, but conspicuous by his absence was Grover Whalen, on whose account the archducal couple had come to Deauville. The famous New Yorker was en route to Switzerland. However, a purported member of his staff remained at the seaside resort and soon a meeting with Franz Josef took place. The Archduke had a farsighted and extraordinary promotional idea.

"It's about your World's Fair," he expounded with enthusiasm. "If Mr. Whalen will empower me to do so, I can interest fifty maharajas from India—all of them fabulously wealthy—to visit the Fair. They could form an outlet for a vast export trade, as every Asiatic potentate buys automobiles, bathtubs, clothes, and spittoons in dozen lots."

It sounded plausible enough, but the American wanted to hear more before communicating with his boss. "How can you do this?" he asked.

Franz Josef showed his credentials as special overseas manager for Cosmopolitan Press, Ltd., of London, publishers of such trade magazines as *World's Press News, Advertising World, Photography Year Book,* and others. In addition he was Asiatic delegate for *Great Britain and the East,* the only British weekly covering India, the Near, Middle and Far East.

The plan took shape then and there. The Whalen party returned to New York that week for a conference with the Fair's directorial board, after which Franz Josef would be notified. It was advisable meanwhile to reserve passage on the *Normandie* for mid-September.

Unfortunately, somewhere between Deauville and Manhattan something went wrong with the idea of the fifty maharajas. Though Grover Whalen himself warmed to it, the board of directors remained cool. In an apologetic cable back to France the Whalen office explained the situation, leaving a slight loophole: if the Archduke cared to come to America as scheduled, another meeting with the commission would be arranged, during which Franz Josef might describe his plan in person.

In the meantime a fresh angle occurred to the enterprising Archduke. At Stonebridge Park offices of the Celotex Company he had met its president, Bror Dahlberg, who was a pioneer in the field of modern building insulation. It had been a simple matter to win Dahlberg as an advertising account for *Great Britain and the East* as well as the World's Fair project, since Asia's greatest need was a weatherproof building material. With America's enormous production of such export goods the possibilities were incalculable.

"Think of the Celotex my fifty maharajas will buy!" was Franz Josef's reaction to the Whalen cable.

That same autumn the archducal couple embarked for New York. A reception committee headed by Mr. Whalen himself awaited them at the French Line's pier and whisked them to Flushing Meadows for an immediate tour of the exhibition. Here they inspected everything from Billy Rose's Aquacade to the excellent Austro-Hungarian restaurant run by Károly Gundel, who was to take root in America as future proprietor of New York's "Hapsburg House."

Having covered the sights, Franz Josef and Marta were fêted as guests of honor at a gigantic luncheon. It was here that Whalen counted on the Archduke's speech which would sway the board of directors into releasing an appropriation for Asiatic propaganda. It also was here that Franz Josef, alas, met his Waterloo. Through a misunderstanding, he believed that the present call for oratory was merely an exchange of courtesies, not to be mixed with business. Certain that a subsequent serious discussion would be arranged, he rose merely to thank the assembled audience for the glorious day he and his wife had experienced, without making reference to so commercial a matter as the maharajas. The result was fatal, as the directors, who had been prepared to hear about maharajas and nothing else, were left high and dry. By the time the demitasse was served, the gentlemen dismissed the project from their minds. The Deauville idea had been given decent burial.

From every other standpoint the American trip was a gratifying success, as the visitors tasted for the first time the boundless measure of New World hospitality. Friends they had known on the Riviera and in Spain reached out welcoming hands. More than that, they opened the doors to their New York and Florida homes, some of which rivaled Europe's castles.

The outstanding experience, however, was a meeting between Franz Josef and Father Flanagan, creator of the famous Boys' Town at Omaha, Nebraska. Here was the antithesis to Brother Saturnino of bitter Bonanova memories. The knowledge that the Church could not be indicted for the sins of an occasional unworthy servant was brought home to him with particular force on viewing the noble work of the Irish-American priest, who happened to have been ordained at the Jesuit University of Innsbruck, Austria.

Another thing became likewise quite clear: life in America was expensive when computed in terms of a slender European income. Though their visitors' permit did not expire for six months, the archducal couple decided to return to Europe early in 1939.

It was the appeasement year of shameful preludes to war, culminating in the debacle of Munich. Franz Josef's one concern now was to get his mother out of Austria before the long-threatening storm at last broke over Europe.

Chapter Thirty

UNDER THE SPREADING SHADOW of the Axis a great exodus of artists, writers, and scientists was taking place. Every liberal-minded European seemed to be pulling up roots, preferring the pangs of exile to the certainty of tyranny at home. Thomas Mann, Albert Einstein, and countless others had long ago formed the vanguard of wandering intellectuals. There followed now a remnant of once repatriated Habsburgs, as well as the Viennese playwright Caesar von Arx, and Hungary's loved composer Emmerich Kálmán.

Before leaving Budapest, Kálmán was summoned to a farewell audience with Admiral Horthy, during which the Regent made a startling comment.

"The whole world ought to become a British colony," he said. "England really *knows* how to govern!"

Lacking this simple solution, the Danube countries were destined to bear the first onslaught of total war. Whoever could finish packing—or, better still, travel light—ought to be on his way.

Among the last to get out of Vienna was the Infanta Blanca, with Dolores, Carlos, and the latter's bride of a few months, Christa Satzger de Bálványos. With the aid of the Spanish Minister, visas had been obtained, permitting the travelers to leave by way of Trieste. Their goal was the Tenuta Reale at Viareggio, as Mama could not finance a longer journey and she refused to accept charity from any of her children. At Tenuta Reale she could still count on a modest income from the vineyards, besides having no rent to pay. Furthermore, the comfortable estate would be a meeting place where she hoped to be reunited with Assunta,

Franz Josef, and perhaps the remaining members of her scattered family.

It was a strange sensation, almost twenty years after that first flight from Wilhelminenberg, to duplicate the Trieste journey. Without a protective husband by her side the Infanta, now past sixty, beheld each landmark as a dramatic milestone in her life. Again, from the deck of a small freighter, she waved farewell to Austria and sailed westward across the Adriatic. She sensed that this was farewell forever. Spread out on a table in her cabin lay the old Emperor Franz Joseph's Golden Jubilee Album, entitled *Viribus Unitis,* with its illustrations by the artist Artur Halmi. Here in review passed all the colorful figures she had once known. Most of them were gone now. Only a few remained still adrift—like herself—uprooted, hunted, in perpetual motion.

Since Italy's participation in World War II was not a certainty, the Infanta hoped to sit out the storm at Viareggio, where time stood still and the tradition of *mezzadria* (equal-share basis) between master and servant had crystallized into a quaint communal pattern. The household and wineries of the archducal estate were run in almost autonomous fashion, with no hard-fisted overseer at the helm. The work went on in placid disinterestedness as all tenants were interdependent upon one another.

On arrival the Infanta knew almost nobody on the place. Many of the older retainers had died, while others, born and reared there, boasted grown offspring of their own. Only one thing remained unchanged: completely at home on their master's premises, the help shuffled about in the same frayed and well-worn pantoufles that had served their forebears long ago. Tenuta Reale was a big place and, as white-haired

Rosalia who presided over its kitchens explained, you got calluses on your feet.

It was Rosalia's husband, old Pietrino, who had given the household a shock some years back. Opposed to innovations, Pietrino had fought with all his might against the installation of a telephone, for he was certain that it could be only an instrument of evil. In fact, so strong was his conviction that, on hearing a voice come over the wire and taking it to be the Devil's, he suffered a heart attack.

Despite such changes, the Infanta counted on finding benevolent neighbors at Viareggio. Immediately adjoining Tenuta Reale lay the estates of the Salviati family, formerly her warm friends. Ten kilometers to the north lay Pianore where the Grand Duchess of Parma lived, née Maria Antonia de Braganza and mother of the Empress Zita. Also, within an hour's drive, was San Rosore, the summer palace of King Victor Emmanuel. Unless Hitler won full domination over Italy, Viareggio would indeed be a pleasant haven.

One grave worry preoccupied the Infanta even as she reached Tenuta Reale. This was the news that Anton and Ileana, now the parents of six children, were under guard at Hollabrunn, unable to leave Austria.

During midsummer of 1938 Queen Marie of Romania had fallen seriously ill, causing physicians to summon Ileana, youngest and perhaps best loved of her ill-assorted children, to her mother's bedside. This was more easily said than done, since German occupation forces curtailed the movements of all Habsburgs who might be pressed into service during the coming struggle; it had not been forgotten that Anton was an experienced pilot. Still, with an eye cocked toward Romanian oil, Nazi authorities relented and permitted the archducal pair to rush to Bucharest. This did not eliminate irritating lengths of red tape which greatly delayed their departure; by the time Anton and Ileana got under way for Sinaïa, precious days had been lost and the Queen lay dying. Even so, with a fast car and each alternating with the other at the wheel, there was a chance to get there in time.

It was a desperate race through Austria and Hungary, then across the border into Transylvania toward the heights of Pelesch. Day and night the travelers sped on, relieving each other at regular intervals. At last, on the morning of July 18, they had come to a final river crossing before Sinaïa. Pausing to wash on the bank of the stream, Anton pulled out his shaving kit to remove a two-day stubble of beard. As he held up a mirror in the pale dawn—it was scarcely five o'clock—his gaze strayed momentarily across the water. There, in the village on the other bank, something fluttered in the breeze. It was the royal standard of Romania flying at half-mast. The Queen was dead.

The rest of that journey called for no further rush. Marie was no longer pressed to see her child. There was plenty of time now. There was all eternity.

During the funeral services at Bucharest the Archduke Anton was able to glean significant information concerning German plans in the Balkans. Better than from any corner inside Austria one could here compute the shrinking interval of peace. He wondered whether it was wise to return to Hollabrunn.

"But the children," Ileana countered as he voiced his thoughts to her; "we have to get back to them——"

He pointed to the temporary travel permit that had been issued for the present trip. On re-entering Austria it would have to be surrendered, with small chance of getting a renewal. Was it not wiser to skip from here to Switzerland

and then send for the children? Surely the little ones would be allowed to move unhampered.

With some misgivings Ileana relented. By plane she and Anton went to Berne, from where they attempted to make contact with their overseer at Castle Sonnberg. But messages were intercepted and they soon learned that their sanguine scheme had led them into a fool's paradise. There was not the slightest chance of a reunion; the children were under supervision by occupation authorities, who would hold them as hostages against their parents' return.

From Switzerland Anton communicated with Franz Josef who, after seeing Mama safely established at Viareggio, planned to return permanently to America.

"We have no further choice," wrote Anton. "You understand that we must go back to Hollabrunn."

Franz Josef wired immediate objections: "Don't go back. Leave with us for America. There are diplomatic channels through which children can be brought out."

The distraught parents of course could give no ear to such a proposal. Without further hesitation they took the next plane home.

"Who knows when we shall see or hear from them again?" said Mama resignedly. Thereafter no mail would come from Hollabrunn, not even from Stepanek, who nowadays was tutor to Anton's children. As in the old days, when the Archduke Pepi had not been able to learn his alphabet unless it was sung to him, Stepanek tuned a squeaky violin and—in a voice grown husky with age—repeated the timeworn lessons:

"A b c d e f g
h i j k lmnop
q r s t u v w

q r s t u v w
  x y z, oh my, oh me—
when will I learn my ABC?"

It was strange how Stepanek's life had become interwoven with that of the archducal family. As a small boy he and his father had walked one Sunday afternoon past the imposing gates of Castle Wilhelminenberg, and the young Karl had asked:

"Who lives here, Papa?"

"The Emperor's kin," had been the elder Stepanek's reply.

"Can I go in and play in the garden?"

"Certainly not! The likes of us don't ever get inside a royal gate——"

Yet, despite his father's gruff and class-conscious warning, Karl Stepanek had spent the best years of his life within such gates, bossing two generations of imperial children.

The Infanta was reminded somehow of Soledad, back in Barcelona. Defiant, proud Doña Sol, who had never had any use for royalty! Married to her Loyalist Pablo, Soledad had recently given birth to a boy, named Leopoldo Vicente after her former Habsburg employer and the child's grand-sire Old Vicente. By mail the Infanta Blanca stood god-mother.

As for Old Vicente, the winged Knight of the Holy Grail, Fate dealt kindly with him. Grown too feeble to shave himself, he doddered twice a week to the neighborhood barber-shop of Pomposo Clucas.

"Pomposo is a great gossip," Soledad wrote to the Infanta, "and as Papa Vicente is too old to read the papers this is the only way he can get all the news."

In any case, on leaving the barber's chair, Vicente's parting remark was always the same:

"*Ya me voy!*" ("I am going!")

Only one day, after having just said that he was going, he did not quite get out of the chair. He was already gone. His spirit had flown no doubt to the heights of Monserrat. . . .

"When one can live and die like Old Vicente," mused the Infanta, "God must be pleased!"

There was not much for God to be pleased about these war-darkened days. Sorrow had begun to strike among the Infanta's children, bringing an awareness of her own approaching old age. No longer did personal danger or discomfort matter much; she contemplated now the suffering of a generation that would supplant her own.

There was the forlorn lot of her eldest daughter Dolores, injured in babyhood through no fault of her own. With beautiful features and a gentle nature, Dolores would nevertheless find it difficult to make her way in a cold and ruthless world. It was Mama's most fervent hope that all the archducal children had absorbed sufficient ethical training to know that they must look after one another in time of trouble. She had taught them to start by showing every consideration to Dolores.

With her married daughters the future looked a trifle more reassuring. There was Immaculata, who with her husband Igino Neri lived at Number 4 Via di Montoro in Rome, whence she made occasional visits to Viareggio. Immaculata continued to be the intellectual in the family; her literary inclinations caused her to uncover numerous interesting facts concerning Mama's brother, the late Carlist Pretender Don Jaime. It appeared that during his long years of exile Uncle Jaime had enjoyed an agreeable—if bookish —friendship with the English novelist Marie Louisa de la Ramée, known as "Ouida." The pseudonym was derived from a childhood attempt to pronounce Louisa. This pro-

lific author of exotic and heavily erotic fiction owned a villa
at Viareggio. Her most famous story, *Under Two Flags,*
with its provocative heroine Cigarette, had been written only
a stone's throw from Tenuta Reale. Similarly, Don Jaime
had cultivated a long and gratifying companionship with
Giacomo Puccini, for the great composer had purchased a
stretch of ground off the Pinetta, the pine-bordered acres
planted years ago by order of the second Don Carlos. It was
thus that on placid summer days the household of Tenuta
Reale could hear the master at work on his piano, as strains
of *Tosca* and *Madame Butterfly* were wafted through open
windows.

Margareta fared perhaps less well than the scholarly Immaculata. Her husband, the Marchese Taliani, had recently
been appointed Italian Ambassador at Shanghai. With
Japan waging an "undeclared" war on China, the fate of
Europeans in the Orient was precarious to say the least.
Italy's future break-away from the Axis would lend weight
to these fears, as the Talianis automatically became enemies
of Japan.

About her son Rainer the Infanta need have no further
worry. Though she mourned him always with the same
intensity, there was at least no anguish over some uncertain
destiny that might becloud his days. She was far more concerned with Leopold, from whom the family had only frag-
mentary news. This much the Infanta knew: Leopold had
married an American named Alicia Coburn and had retired
to a life of utmost privacy in New England.

Another of her children transplanted to the Western
Hemisphere was Maria Antonia, that romantic Mimi who
had been the central figure of the Balearic journey years ago.
Widowed in the course of Spain's Civil War, Mimi had fled,
with four young daughters and a son, from her Mallorca

home to seek refuge in South America, where she was known simply as Señora de Orlandis.

There remained Anton, unable to depart from his Nazi-guarded castle, and Assunta, the nun who had returned to worldly estate. And lastly, there were the two Benjamins—Franz Josef and Carlos—to occupy the Infanta's thoughts. They were all grown and independent, freed of forgotten nursery bonds. Yet she was aware that none would find the going easy, for the day had passed when parents could insure their children's future. In the coming storm she would be unable to shield them. She would be helpless herself.

Chapter Thirty-One

As SHE REVIEWED the varied fortunes of her children, Mama
reflected that Assunta was destined perhaps to find the greatest happiness. For it was in her youngest daughter that the
Infanta saw her own far-reaching judgment confirmed.

A remarkable transformation had taken place in the erstwhile nun. Still youthful, Assunta was slim and beautifully
built, like all the Toscana Habsburgs. Nor had monastic
vows annihilated her fundamental zest for living. After lay-
ing aside her religious trappings, the unfrocked nun romped
through the gardens of Tenuta Reale in Tyrolean woolens
and peaked hat of green felt trimmed with a fine upstanding
chamois brush.

In part this change may have been attributable to the
presence of Marta, Franz Josef's lovely wife, who created a
sensation in Viareggio. Assunta was dazzled from the start
by her new sister-in-law. It had been a long time since she
had beheld feminine beauty of any but the saccharine type
perpetuated in religious portraiture. Marta was no madonna:
she was a golden-haired and very pagan Venus. What was
more, she awakened in other women the longing to be
beautiful themselves.

At first Assunta had resisted this longing. Her piety
fought against worldliness and the sinful promptings of
vanity. But daily her armor grew weaker as the pulsating
life around her impinged upon the girl's consciousness. Before too long, vanity won. Assunta joined her sister-in-law
on a shopping trip. In another month the former nun
thought nothing of donning shorts and going bicycling
along the strand.

To cap all this, Assunta fell presently in love.

There was at Viareggio a refugee physician from Poland who had begun to set up a promising practice in competition with the town's all but retired veteran *Dottore* del Prete.

"It's high time we had a new doctor," said local dowagers in praise of the younger man. "Old del Prete isn't much use except for a good afternoon of gossip."

This was true. The octogenarian medico did little more than chat with his patients or sit at home and read music out of yellowed opera libretti. Though he played no instrument, del Prete was something of a critic, and a passionate admirer of Verdi. Only once—in error—did he pick up a score of *Lohengrin* and peruse a few pages before realizing that he was being contaminated by an unclassical German composer. Reluctantly he conceded to his son Lino that night:

"Ho letto un pezzetino di Wagner—non c'e male, non c'e male!" ("I have read a bit of Wagner—not bad, not bad!")

For his patients, however, the graybeard's increasing indifference to medical subjects had become a hazard; there was no telling when del Prete might prescribe a symphony concert in place of a needed cathartic. In consequence the arrival of the Polish colleague had been greeted with enthusiasm by the town in general and Assunta in particular. Indeed, the subsequent romance elicited some acid comments on the part of Viareggio society, loath to lose the indispensable bachelor.

It was no trivial flirtation. The erstwhile bride of Christ, who still wore the Teresiana ring on her fourth finger, meant to exchange a new set of vows. She planned to trade her nun's cowl for a sprig of orange blossoms.

It happened that she did not encounter fair sailing, as Mama was strict and none too encouraging toward strange young men. Assunta met her doctor on the sly, while walk-

Shrine of St. Thérèse of Lisieux, marking New Hampshire property of Archduke Franz Josef.

Timberland around Franconia, New Hampshire.

smiles playing on their lips were of a special brand known as a Cheshire cat's.

The subject of babies, incidentally, was one of the Infanta's major preoccupations. She believed in motherhood and made no bones about her disappointment in the modern world's declining birth rate, viewing even Ileana's brood of six as a puny effort. At family gatherings, daughters and daughters-in-law were accustomed to Mama's frank scrutiny of their figures to ascertain whether they were *enceinte*. Indeed her obstetric interest extended beyond immediate Habsburg circles as she campaigned for crowded nurseries at home and abroad. During a Cannes visit she was heard to remark, in heavily accented English, to a rich London bride:

"So you sit in your castle. So you 'av nossing to do. Vy not you make a child?"

It was excellent advice, much needed in a world that was fast forgetting the true source of happiness. Moreover the Infanta did not lack suitably harrowing support in ancient folklore with which to bolster her argument. To this Englishwoman she quoted a Spanish superstition:

"A childless wife, later she goes out of the mind—they put her in a lunatic!"

This ought to be enough to rouse the most atrophied maternal impulse.

Another matter in which Mama took pride nowadays was her increasing ability to get along without domestic help. Since the days of Soledad in Barcelona, she had not been able to afford a personal maid; at her cramped Vienna apartment she would indeed have had no room for one. Learning to do her own puttering, she liked to boast:

"I have the quickest servant! I ring the bell—and here I am already!" Yes, there she was indeed. It was wonderful.

Luckily this adaptability had been transmitted to her children, who would have reason to make use of it in a swiftly changing world. Franz Josef, for one, was striking out boldly along new paths; he sailed with Marta aboard the Italian liner *Conte di Savoia* on September 15, 1939, for America, twelve days after Prime Minister Chamberlain declared England at war.

The parting, at Viareggio, was less perfunctory than on their previous voyage, for both Franz Josef and his wife knew that this time they were not going on a mere visit. They hoped to find a home in the New World. This meant saying good-by to much that they held dear, family ties, friends, places, and memories. They knew it would take a share of industry and courage to make a fresh start against odds they could not yet measure.

Up to the last moment Franz Josef continued in his efforts to persuade his relatives to tear up roots and flee from Europe while there was still time. But his best arguments failed in the face of their stoic determination to remain, each in his sphere of duty. Anton and Ileana would not be separated from their children, while Mama refused to be dislodged from Tenuta Reale, the last place where she did not have to be a financial burden to anyone. Besides, the Infanta was getting on in years; at her age the prospect of being transplanted from one continent to another held nothing but terror for her wearied spirit. She wanted to wind up her days where she had spent the happiest of them—in Europe, come what may.

Of course if Mama did not budge, the invalid Dolores had no choice but to remain, which automatically placed upon Carlos a responsibility that was not to be dodged. Carlos had been mother's pampered darling through years when the older boys had left the nest and gone out to battle for a living. Today the time for a squaring of accounts had come: Carlos faced a lasting obligation. He must stay behind not only to aid the aging Ferrari in running the affairs of Tenuta Reale, but as a protector for the three women—Mama, Dolores, and Christa, his bride.

As for Marta's family ties, there was only one. Her parents had died and she had no one left in Vienna save an adored sister, Irma, who was ill of cancer. Irma had been a pianist of great promise, but her career was ended. Only one thing could be done for her: one must provide money to pay doctors, nurses, radium treatments—all of which admittedly could not halt but only ease her departure from this life. To transport Irma overseas would have been needless torment; but she was flown to London, where monthly drafts cabled from New York would provide for her upkeep. It was for Irma as much as for her own safety that Marta longed to reach America.

The *Conte di Savoia* entered New York harbor on September 23, docking at the Italian Line's Hudson pier.

This time no reception committee crowded the dock, nor did a caravan of official cars lead the way to the splendors of a World's Fair. Filing down the gangplank with their fellow travelers, the archducal couple entered the United States without fanfare. They expected nothing else. Franz Josef did not consider himself a representative of a once great and prosperous ruling house, nor a celebrity to be paraded on exhibition before a Flushing Meadows crowd. But neither was he an impecunious refugee throwing himself upon the charity of a strange land. Through his own savings, plus such funds as his wife had managed to salvage, he would be able to weather the transition from a life reckoned in humble pesetas or lire to the standards of a more frightening currency, the potent dollar. Natu-

rally such savings could not last long; once the Archduke had established residence he would look for work.

New York appeared a wise choice for people who knew
only the rudiments of English. Marta's currently most
prized possession was a copy of Webster's Dictionary, bound
in green and gold leather like some rare Chaucerian item.
Manhattan was a cosmopolitan place, where every language
in the world could be heard within the cramped area between the Bowery and the Bronx.

Also, New York was filled with repatriated Americans
who had been part of the international set of London, Paris,
Rome, and the Côte d'Azur. Among them the archducal
couple recognized numerous loyal companions of other
years, notably the American-born Duchess de Talleyrand-
Périgord, née Anna Gould, former wife of Marquis Boni
de Castellane. Through her Franz Josef and Marta found
a gracious welcome such as they could not otherwise have
dreamed of. For the Duchess, alone since her children were
grown and had left the roost, threw open her doors to
stranded acquaintances, British war orphans, shipwrecked
merchants, deserving refugees, or just agreeable friends. To
the archducal pair she offered one of the vacant gardeners'
cottages on the magnificent Jay Gould estate at Tarrytown
on the Hudson, where with some architectural changes and
abundant wielding of a paint brush a bit of Austrian baroque
took shape. Under this hospitable roof it would be pleasant
indeed to sit out the storm of World War II, now bursting
upon mankind in its full fury.

To be sure, Franz Josef wanted to do very little sitting.
Having entered the United States under a visitor's permit,
he could not seek a salaried job which might rob an American workman of his livelihood. But under the law he was

Archduchess Franz Josef of Austria as a young girl.

Archduchess Franz Josef in New York.

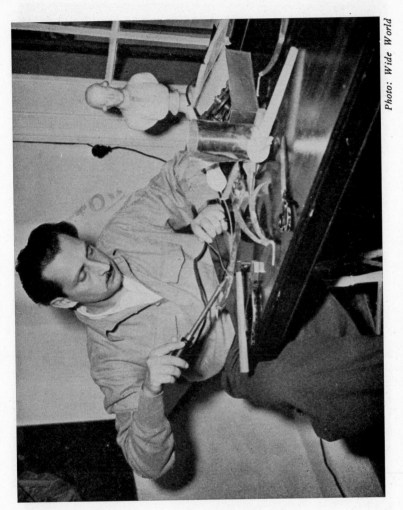

Photo: Wide World

Franz Josef making candle holder from old tin cans, for his American home.

"Lyndhurst Cottage," after being transformed into Austrian Baroque.

permitted to earn commissions on sales of any kind or to make money by writing newspaper articles and stories which, after some polishing and editing at the hands of professional experts, appeared in *Collier's, Liberty* and *Esquire*. One such article drew a letter to the editor from Mr. Sam Murray of Miami, Florida. It ran:

"I hope the story (March 23, *Liberty*) written by Archduke Franz Josef proved as interesting to your other readers as it did to me, but I doubt it. My main interest is in the author, the young archduke who got his first job working in the Ford Plant in Barcelona, Spain, when I was managing the Spanish Ford Company about fifteen years ago.

"We wondered if this handsome young aristocrat was not looking for a pension because of his family name, so we put him to work on what we know as the body line, stuffing upholstery and tacking the imitation leather to the body frames. It didn't take us long to learn that he was asking no consideration because of his birthright.

"With the experiences of having been more or less a professional exile, this same Franz Josef can possibly tell you many interesting tales.

"SAM MURRAY"

Despite his literary dabblings, the transplanted Habsburg did not have the presumption to fancy himself an author, but he was profoundly grateful for the chance to wield a gainful pen. In this manner he could mark time until the State Department studied his case and issued some directive permitting him to hold a job. When it was granted in 1943, Franz Josef underwent examinations as a registered representative of the New York Stock Exchange and became a Wall Street breadwinner.

But his activity did not end there. While Marta plunged into war work, first for the British Ambulance Corps and later for every related American war charity—she also regularly donated blood—the Archduke began the spiritual sloughing off of European ties. For one thing, the first U.S. Draft Registration was being held on October 16, 1940, from which many foreigners believed themselves exempt. Franz Josef interpreted the draft as a call for all able-bodied men in the country, regardless of nationality or citizenship, hence he reported at once. Wanting to lead the line in his particular district, he appeared at 183 East Sixty-sixth Street, where applicants were to sign, at 6:30 A.M., though the doors did not open till 8:00. But he was disappointed to find another early riser who had squatted on a campstool since dawn; the Archduke was obliged to stand in second place. As the building, a school, at last opened, the first arrival broke his silence to point out that he would like to sign before anyone else. Franz Josef nodded and inquired if the other was likewise a foreigner.

"No," replied the young man, "I am an American."

At this the Archduke beamed. He no longer stood in second place. He was truly the first alien in his district to offer his services to the United States.

Throughout those early months of adjustment Franz Josef and Marta found American hospitality true to its reputation. Old friends and those newly made helped to arouse in them a feeling of home. The Archduke's next dream, premature and overambitious perhaps, was to own a piece of America where, after the war, he and Marta might hope to take root. Unlike thousands of purely temporary refugees who waited only for the moment when they could rush back to their former haunts, Franz Josef's purpose was to settle in the United States.

That he should look for a corner which most nearly

evoked the unforgotten beauty of his native Austria was only natural. That he should find it in sober, rural New England was miraculous. There in the pine-covered mountain country of New Hampshire, near the picturesque town of Franconia, all the smiling loveliness of the Salzburg region, the Semmering, and the Tyrol seemed to have been recaptured. Here was a goal to work for. Such earnings as America granted him he meant to invest in a patch of New Hampshire earth.

As a step toward the realization of this dream, he created and became a partner in the Franconia Lumber and Development Company, headed by a former governor of the New York Stock Exchange, Mr. William V. C. Ruxton. Apart from furnishing wood pulp for wartime needs, this enterprise included plans for a great postwar skiing and summer fishing resort.

To assure good fortune to the undertaking, Franz Josef nailed to a silver birch a *"Marterl"* (holy image) of Saint Thérèse de Lisieux. This was the younger Saint Thérèse or Little Flower, of Alençon (1873-1897), rather than the Carmelite Teresa de Avila in Old Castile (1515-1582) after whom Assunta's convent had been named. With such pious intercession the Archduke felt that his highest hopes could not fail to be realized.

New Hampshire visits for the present were by no means devoted to religious meditation or the contemplation of an agreeable landscape. The Franconia Lumber and Development Company was itself in its developing stage, calling for sweat and muscle. However kindly she might be disposed, Saint Thérèse could not be called upon to engage in actual work. With a labor shortage and the wartime limitation on agricultural implements, the Archduke donned working togs and shouldered an ax for a daily twelve-hour tussle in the woods.

To facilitate new and for the most part rustic contacts, he spared Franconia natives the annoyance of a foreign title. In New Hampshire he was greeted by township judge or fellow woodcutter as Joe Franz.

Chapter Thirty-Two

EARLY IN 1941 Franz Josef received an appeal from his sister Assunta, asking if he could facilitate entry into the United States for her and her small family. With the course of the war thus far strongly favoring the Axis, life in Spain had become increasingly difficult for the Austrian Archduchess and her Polish husband. What added to their plight was the fact that they had no means whatever to finance an escape. Perhaps Franz Josef could help?

He was in no position to issue transatlantic tickets at random among his numerous kin. Yet Assunta's need could not be denied. He must find a way of bringing her to safety.

After thorough investigation, immigration authorities issued a visa permitting entry, provided Franz Josef guaranteed that neither his sister nor her family would become a burden to U.S. charity. With some apprehension, in view of his own uncertain future, he gave these guarantees and set about making the necessary travel arrangements.

It now developed that in view of the submarine threat it was no longer safe to cross the Atlantic by boat, except under naval convoy. This left only one possible choice: one of the weekly planes from Portugal. The former nun reached the peak of her emancipation—she took to the air by Clipper. The baby Marie Thérèse, held in her mother's arms, became the youngest passenger ever booked for the Lisbon-New York flight.

Assunta took the New World likewise in her stride. Settling down to the simplest possible existence, she waited patiently for her husband to master English and pass the difficult examinations that would entitle him to practice medicine in a strange land. At the same time she awaited the arrival of her second child, Elisabeth Stefanie, delivered in New York on December 5, 1942. This little girl is the first direct descendant of Habsburg lineage to be born in North America.

As for the guarantees provided by Franz Josef, they proved happily unnecessary. The small family became quickly acclimatized and learned to fend for itself. The Infanta Blanca had been right to the last: Assunta did not belong behind convent walls. She was eminently able to cope with the world.

If she had been right about Assunta, had Mama chosen well for herself? Did she act wisely in remaining at Viareggio?

This question plagued Franz Josef through each advancing month of the war. After 1942, when German occupation forces took over the management of Mussolini's Italy, no news whatever reached him from his relatives. Tenuta Reale like Hollabrunn, where Anton and Ileana lived in "protective custody," was under military guard.

With the landing of American troops—first in Sicily and later on the Italian mainland—the situation changed. Town after town fell under Allied bombardment, causing Nazi forces to roll backward in a gigantic retreat. It was now that the iron grip on Viareggio relaxed, though the danger of shelling and destruction continued as Allied naval units converged upon near-by Elba. Their next target was sure to be the long beach front of Tenuta Reale.

In the wake of the fleeing Germans anarchy spread through the abandoned towns as a starving citizenry engaged in unhampered looting. Behind curtained windows the Infanta Blanca peered out at the same scenes of violence and dissolution that she had witnessed—how many years ago?—in Vienna. Why did revolt and war wear always the same face?

She did not know the answer. But her proud spirit bowed at last to necessity. She agreed to leave her only remaining earthly possession, Tenuta Reale, behind. Stripped now of everything, she was ready to take flight.

Beside her stood Dolores, Christa, and Carlos—Carlos holding his one-year-old daughter Alexandra. As on a similar occasion at Castle Wilhelminenberg, when Carlos himself had been a child, they wore travel clothes and carried only the barest necessities crammed into a small bag. By nightfall they would slip outside and make their escape to Genoa by car, whence they hoped to embark for Barcelona. Spain, sapped by years of political strife, was not an ideal place of refuge, but the changing fortunes of war had dimmed Axis influence in the West. Britain's Churchill, with a shrewd eye to the Empire's commercial future, had of late stroked Franco's fur most placatingly. The hand of Hitler no longer reached far enough for a similar caress, hence fugitive Habsburgs might dwell south of the Pyrenees in reasonable safety.

It was prior to this flight that the Infanta wrote a letter to Franz Josef. It ran:

"Mon cher Pepi!
"Perhaps this note will not reach you, but I must write it because last night I had a dreadful dream about you—it was happiness just to awaken!

"I think so much about you, who were so kind (*gentil*) as a child and a young man. Things go well enough for me, though I don't know if I shall last through the war. Still, maybe I can. . . .

"It is good to know that Assunta is near you and that you can all look after one another. Tell Assunta not to forget the virtues she learned at home, in the Sacré Coeur, and during her life as a nun. Now she has a husband to devote herself to with body and soul. The small Thérèse is ravishing, to judge from pictures. How is the second one? How sad it is for a mother and grandmother to see all those she loves dispersed over the earth!

"Dolores is well, thank God.

"I embrace you and Marta with all my heart,

"MAMAN"

A pause followed upon this letter, during which Franz Josef was tormented by uncertainty regarding the fate of his family. But on March 22, 1944, after more than a year of silence, Carlos at last was heard from. He wrote from the Catalan capital:

"Dear Franz Josef:

"At last, after interminable delays and hardships, we have arrived in Barcelona. We are all well, except for Mama who is very weary and nervous. She is in the care of Soledad (loyal through all these years!) and sees almost no one.

"Since July of 1943 we were completely cut off from all outside contact. The house at Tenuta Reale was still standing when we left, but Viareggio itself looks like a wild neglected village. Funny people, gangsters. The place is almost depopulated.

"The last we heard of Mac [Immaculata] she was with Igino below Rome, but they have nothing to eat. After train connections with the south were cut I sent her a load of canned goods by truck just before we left.

"Meg [Margareta] and Francesco are in a Japanese concentration camp since Italy joined the Allies; I am trying to intercede for them through Madrid, but it looks difficult. From Anton we have no news whatever.

"I am so happy to be able to write you and Marta, and to know that you are all safe. Is Leo [Leopold] still in New England? Do you hear from Mimi [Maria Antonia]?

"What will Otto do, now that Hungary too is lost?

Maybe we should all become sausage makers and open what I am told is called in America a Hot Dog Stand. . . .

"Everything seems marvelous to us here. We can't get over admiring the food, automobiles, lighted streets and well-dressed people—after the shabbiness we have grown used to. Barcelona has not changed much, except that cars use wood for fuel instead of gasoline. We own no car of course, having auctioned off the old one—*quien da más* [who gives more]—at the docks in Genoa before we sailed.

"The house in Viareggio may not survive the war. At present it is occupied by Italian troops, for which we must be grateful; it would otherwise be plundered by the mob as were all the better homes in the town. During recent years the grounds looked lovely; I had done much cultivating by tractor. Now all that is finished and belongs to the past.

"For Mama it is the third or actually fourth escape from war: first Austria, then Spain, Austria again, and now this. The strain has been too much and we are worried about her health. Dolores lives with us now.

"Christa and the baby send many hugs. Please write me at once, as I have such a longing to hear from all of you.
"Your brother,

"CARLOS"

As he read, Franz Josef caught again the echo of a world profoundly loved, yet grown strangely dim and distant: a world in which picturesque figures of history had walked upon a glittering and often blood-spattered stage. Yet one by one they had vanished of themselves, even as Mama's generation, though still inhabiting its mortal shell, was moving beyond reach. Not space or separation caused this thing, but time itself. For Dolores, never away from the Infanta's side, would lose her too. The most tightly closed fist in the end holds nothing.

What could be asked then of the fragile bonds that linked together the remaining brothers and sisters, except that the inexorable race against time be stayed for yet another while?

Letters, small written words such as Carlos had put on paper, sustained those bonds that joined today's thoughts with yesterday's memories and had the power to evoke a nursery of ten boisterous children who somehow were no more.

The miracle of words and thoughts and memories! The wonder of a letter or a book! Springing from seeming nothingness, they held the laughter and passion and tragedy of all existence. Were they perhaps the one glorious proof that "nothingness" did not exist, or rather, is eternally pregnant with promise of that which is to come? Life itself in its moment of inception springs out of that mysteriously creative vacuum into which all "things" born of "nothing" must return.

Then no form of nostalgia is unique. Uprooted souls fall victims to it as surely as those who never have left home. Here at last, Franz Josef knew, was the common enemy, attacking all mankind and binding each fate to every other fate. The proud, the humble, the rich, the poor, were haunted by forgotten melodies of songs heard long ago, yet never to be recaptured.

In the dance of life the crowded ballroom grew empty of itself. The waltz did not go on forever: it faded softly, and was lost. . . .

THE END

INDEX

Index

Date Due

3908	] Jul 2		
5765	Jul 16		
APR 12 1975			
⑬			